Chemistry Experiments for High School

Christina H. Swan

John D. Mays

NOVARE
SCIENCE & MATH

Austin, Texas
2014

Published by
NOVARE SCIENCE & MATH LLC
P. O. Box 92934
Austin, Texas 78709-2934
novarescienceandmath.com

Printed in the United States of America

ISBN: 978-0-9904397-6-9

Cover design by Nada Orlic, http://nadaorlic.info/

For the complete catalog of textbooks and resources available from Novare Science & Math, visit novarescienceandmath.com.

About the Authors

Christina H. Swan has been teaching Molecular Biology, Advanced Biology, and Advanced Chemistry at Regents School of Austin in Austin, Texas for over five years. She received her Bachelor of Science in biology from Westmont College. She earned her Ph.D. at the University of California at San Diego in the field of molecular pathology.

John D. Mays is the owner and founder of Novare Science and Math. He spent 15 years as an engineer in industry and has been teaching science and mathematics for 18 years, mostly at Regents School of Austin. He received his Bachelor of Science in electrical engineering from Texas A&M University. Subsequently he earned Master of Education and Master of Liberal Arts degrees, and completed 36 hours in graduate study in physics.

Acknowledgement

Thanks, once again, to Dr. Chris Mack for his thoughtful and very helpful review of the manuscript.

Contents

Welcome

A laboratory practicum incorporating a series of quantitative experiments is an essential component of any high school or college chemistry course. It is one thing to read about precipitations; it is another thing to see the precipitates form with your own eyes. Again, it is one thing to talk about the dramatic change in solution pH near the equivalence point of a titration, it is another to see how quickly the pH changes and to see the change in indicator color that occurs at the same time.

In addition to seeing the reactions first hand, laboratory experience provides the student with practice using standard laboratory apparatus and methods. Modern chemistry is a discipline born in the laboratory, and the test tubes, graduated cylinders, and Bunsen burners used in a chemistry lab are familiar to nearly everyone who has completed a formal education. We remember an occasion when our head of school nearly lost his cool when he discovered that some juniors in the Rhetoric class he was teaching did not know what a test tube was. The topic at hand was *in vitro* fertilization, and our head of school had used the phrase "test-tube baby," only to find that several students did not know what he meant. He raced down to the lab, grabbed a few test tubes, and stormed back to his classroom to inform the students of what their science education had apparently failed to inform them. These days, the experience gained in a chemistry lab can make a difference in a person's ability simply to follow an article in a newspaper!

Finally, there is nothing like laboratory practice to give students a feel for how the stoichiometric calculations learned in the classroom relate to the predictions and results of an actual experiment. Experienced teachers all know that when a student encounters a subject in several different ways and through various means, the learning outcomes are far superior to those that result when a student encounters a subject in only one way or through a limited number of means. Accordingly, students will *learn* chemistry at a deeper level and *remember* chemical principles longer if they experience the subject through both the classroom and the laboratory.

The 20 experiments in this volume will expose students to the practical aspects associated with the broad array of topics that occur in a first-year chemistry course. We encourage you to incorporate as many of these experiments as possible into your own students' experience of the subject.

Preface for Teachers

Introduction

It should be obvious to any science teacher in the 21st century that safety, chemical storage, and chemical disposal are issues that must be treated very seriously and thoroughly in school science labs. It is not the intention of this book to offer complete details on these important matters. But since many of the teachers who will be using this book in their classrooms may be relatively new in their roles as science teachers, we will review some of the most important issues you should address in order for your science lab to be safe and environmentally sound.

Again, this book is not a laboratory safety or design manual and the information here is far from exhaustive. We have found the resources at Flinn Scientific to be very thorough and helpful. Acquire a copy of the Flinn Scientific catalog. In the back of this catalog is the most exhaustive set of guidelines for safety, lab design, chemical storage, and waste disposal that we know of. It is an excellent resource.

We recommend reading some of the books you will find in the Flinn Scientific catalog such as *Prudent Practices in the Laboratory*, *CRC Handbook of Laboratory Safety*, *Science Laboratory Safety Manual*, and *Safety in Academic Chemistry Laboratories*.

We also encourage you to spend some time looking at the materials under the Teacher Resources tab at flinnsci.com—a veritable treasure trove of information. Flinn Scientific can also function as a one-stop-shop for safety supplies, storage cabinets, storage bottles, labels, and other supplies.

The experiments in this book are designed for use in a fully-equipped chemistry lab. Those that do not have access to a laboratory may wish to examine our other experiments manual, *Chemistry Experiments for High School at Home* (*CEHSH*). The experiments in *CEHSH* do require special chemicals and apparatus—for students to have a quantitative chemistry laboratory experience there is just no way around it. But the experiments in *CEHSH* have been designed to minimize the expense for apparatus and chemicals as far as possible.

Chemistry Texts

This manual has been designed to accompany either of two chemistry texts written by John D. Mays and published by Novare Science and Math: *General Chemistry* and *Chemistry for Accelerated Students*. At the beginning of each experiment in this book you will find references to content in both of these texts pertaining to the experiment. Exceptions are Experiments 13 and 14, which address topics covered only in *Chemistry for Accelerated Students*.

Laboratory Safety

It is the laboratory instructor's responsibility to ensure that all substances are handled and used safely. This responsibility includes proper clean up, disposal, and storage of chemicals, glassware and other materials. Some general safety practices are as follows:

1. Always wear appropriate protective goggles or face shield, gloves, and laboratory apron when working with chemicals or flames.

2. Keep the Safety Data Sheet (SDS)—formerly known as the Material Safety Data Sheet (MSDS)—for every chemical in your lab. The SDS is supplied with the chemical when it is purchased. Read the SDS for every chemical you use, and take note of information about

toxicity, vapors, and other concerns that will require special precautions.

3. Supply your lab with all necessary safety equipment. This includes:

    a. Fire extinguisher, ABC dry type
    b. Fire blanket
    c. Eye wash station
    d. Shower station
    e. Secure, ventilated storage for chemicals (see below)
    f. Protective eyewear for everyone in the room
    g. Laboratory aprons for everyone in the room
    h. Gloves for everyone in the room, including heat-resistant gloves for handling hot materials and nitrile gloves for handling most chemicals
    i. A special container for broken glass (Flinn Scientific has an inexpensive one.)

4. Instruct students to follow laboratory instructions carefully.

5. Warn students against unauthorized mixing of chemicals.

6. Accidents in labs are caused by carelessness, silliness, or improper procedures. Warn students against these.

7. Instruct students to follow all safety precautions in the lab. A list of safety rules for students to study is in the Preface for Students.

8. Arrange for appropriate chemical storage, disposal containers, and procedures before the lab activity begins.

Chemical Storage

No chemicals should be stored in unsecured cabinets except items children under 18 years of age can purchase at a grocery store. Everything else should be stored in locked cabinets in a climate-controlled, continuously ventilated storage room. Arrange for each of the following in your chemical storage area:

1. *Secure storage* — Students must not have access to chemicals except under the supervised, controlled conditions of a laboratory exercise. All chemicals should be stored in locking storage cabinets.

2. *Appropriate cabinets* — Separate locking storage cabinets should be supplied for flammables, acids, and other chemicals. Acid cabinets should be entirely free of metal, and flammables cabinets should be designed to prevent flammables from coming into contact with sources of ignition. Cabinets for general chemicals should have many different shelves to allow for compatible chemicals to be stored together (see below). Shelves in general chemical cabinets should have lips on the front to help prevent tipped-over bottles from rolling off the shelf onto the floor.

3. *Climate controlled* — High temperatures will rapidly degrade many compounds, rendering them useless. Thus, chemical storage needs to be in a climate-controlled environment.

4. *Proper ventilation* — Regardless of the quality of your containers, there will be fumes in a chemical storage area. For this reason the store room must be incorporated into a properly designed HVAC system that supplies fresh air. Additional emergency ventilation is also a good idea.

5. *Chemical separation*   Chemicals that can react dangerously together should not be stored together. There is always the possibility of a damaged or leaking storage container. Flinn Scientific has a Storage Patterns guideline to help you segregate chemicals on chemical cabinet storage shelves.

6. *Identification*   You should never have unidentified bottles of chemicals in the lab. Purchase plastic or glass containers and label them with the name of the chemical, the concentration (if solution), major safety concerns, and the date prepared. Further, use the Compatible Chemical Families Bottle Labels available from Flinn Scientific. The Compatible Chemical Families labels correlate to the Suggested Storage Patterns (see above) so that chemicals are stored together with compatible chemicals and away from incompatible chemicals. Labeling bottles appropriately and following appropriate storage patterns is an important factor in accident prevention.

7. *Neatness*   As important as classroom appearance is, keeping your laboratory areas tidy and well-organized is much more than a matter of appearance. A tidy, well-organized laboratory is another important factor in accident prevention.

Prep Room

In a chemistry lab you need space for a lot of different prep and cleanup operations, and a separate prep room is the best way to provide space for these activities. Again, visit flinnsci.com for more detailed lab design information.

Waste Disposal

No school chemistry laboratory can operate without reckoning with proper waste collection and disposal procedures. Very few substances can be washed down the drain without some kind of pre-treatment, and many substances cannot be washed down the drain at all. *It is the laboratory instructor's responsibility to ensure that all substances are disposed of properly.* Today, chemistry instructors must contend with a complex labyrinth of federal, state, and local regulations regarding disposal of chemicals. Getting good information about waste disposal is difficult, but fortunately, Flinn Scientific again comes to our aid. In the back of the Flinn Scientific catalog is a section entitled Chemical Disposal Procedures. This is an invaluable resource, quite thorough and loaded with detail. Before performing any of the experiments in this book, review the correct disposal procedures for the chemicals used in the experiment and obtain any supplies or containers you will need. Incorporate the clean up and disposal activities into your lab time—don't put it off until later. Disposal procedures such as acid-base neutralization and precipitation are important for students to know about. Involving the students in the cleanup and disposal after an experiment will give them valuable additional experience, save you time, and help keep your laboratory safe and tidy.

Percent Difference Calculation

Several of the experiments in this book require students to calculate a "percent difference." Refer to the Preface for Students for details on this calculation.

Lab Reports and Lab Journals

High school science teachers should require that students write full-length lab reports from scratch, on a computer, five or six times per year. In *Teaching Science so that Students Learn Science*, John Mays devoted a chapter to laboratory work and lab reports. That chapter outlines assessment guidelines and learning objectives for lab reports at different grade levels throughout high school.

There is a lot that goes into writing a quality lab report, and teaching students how to do it without a guide to help is a very difficult and time-consuming task. Thus, we commend to your students John Mays' manual, *The Student Lab Report Handbook*. We recommend that schools distribute copies at the beginning of the school year to each high school freshman. Let each student keep the book for use at home for the next four years. Students should begin learning how to write lab reports in their freshman science class, and they should continue writing reports in all science classes throughout their high school years. Students trained this way will astonish their lab instructors when they get to college, and will be prepared for college in a way few students are.

Students in high school chemistry courses typically conduct at least 15 or 20 lab exercises during the year. But requiring students to write 15 or 20 lab reports from scratch in a year would not be reasonable. This is why we recommend requiring students to write reports from scratch five or six times during the year—three times in the fall and three times in the spring. For other experiments, use a short-form lab report in which students present data and interact with a few key questions. At the end of each experiment in this book there are a few pages that may be used as a short-form lab report. The book is printed on perforated sheets that can be written on, removed from the book, and submitted. This provision is *not* intended to suggest that all the experiments should be documented this way. But for those that are, the book makes short-form reports easy.

During their laboratory activities students need to develop the skill of keeping a proper lab journal. *The Student Lab Report Handbook* contains a detailed description of using a lab journal. Information about both of the books we have mentioned in this section is on our website, novarescienceandmath.com.

Precision in Measurements

Naturally, all experimental measurements should be made with as much precision as possible. For volume measurements made with a graduated cylinder, this typically means measuring to the nearest 0.1 mL. With a buret, 0.01 mL precision should be the norm.

For mass measurements, the precision will depend on the digital mass balances you have in the lab. For measuring small masses, we strongly encourage you to furnish students with digital mass balances that can read to 0.001 g. If your budget does not allow this, then 0.01 g resolution should be regarded as an absolute minimum of precision. Other balances should also be available in the lab for measuring larger masses of up to 200 g and 2 kg, and lower-priced models of such balances typically limit precision to 0.1 g or 0.01 g.

In this manual, we assume all students have access to a balance that can measure to at least 0.01 g. When we use the phrase "0.01 g or better," we mean "to the nearest 0.01 g at least, and to the nearest 0.001 g if possible."

Preface for Students

Introduction

The laboratory component in a chemistry course is very important. As we explained on the Welcome page, experiments are your opportunity to have direct experience with phenomena that are difficult to appreciate simply from reading about them in a book. Additionally, you will remember your chemistry much better if you encounter the principles in both in the text and in the lab. But when we get involved with chemistry experiments, we are very often dealing with substances that can be very dangerous if not handled correctly. For this reason, the information in this Preface is very important. In chemistry experiments our highest concerns are for ensuring the safety of everyone in the room and being responsible for proper disposal of waste so that toxic substances are not released into the environment.

Safety Procedures

It is very important that you learn the following safety procedures and follow them conscientiously:

1. If you are heating substances on a hot plate or over a flame, you should always wear safety goggles or safety glasses.

2. When handling hot substances or apparatus, use tongs or wear heat-resistant gloves.

3. Use great care when handling glassware. As we always say, there are three ways to break something—improper procedures, silliness, or carelessness—and all are bad in a lab!

4. Wear protective eyewear, gloves, and a laboratory apron when handling hazardous materials. Wear a face shield when handling concentrated acids.

5. Make sure you have a phone in your work area in case you ever need to call for help.

6. Always follow written procedures, and don't take short cuts. Do not revise procedures to suit yourself without consulting with a responsible and knowledgeable person who knows about the kind of work you are attempting to perform.

7. Never taste things in a science lab unless your instructor directs you to.

8. Always keep long hair tied back out of the way, and don't wear loose, blowsy, or baggy clothing while working in a lab.

9. Make sure there is adequate ventilation in your work area.

10. Make sure you have a fire extinguisher in your work area.

11. Exercise care in everything you do, pay attention, and avoid horseplay.

12. When preparing solutions of acids and bases, always pour the concentrated acid or base into pure water. Do not ever pour water into concentrated acid or base solutions. When acids or bases are mixed with water, a great deal of heat is released. Pouring into water disperses the acid or base into the water where the heat can be absorbed. Otherwise, the heat produced can cause dangerous flash boiling and splashing of the concentrated acid or base.

13. If smelling the vapors of a substance is part of your procedure, always gently waft the vapors toward your nose with your hand. Do not sniff vapors by placing your nose into a container where vapors may be concentrated.

14. Treat unknown substances as if they were flammable, corrosive, or toxic.

15. Keep your work area tidy. If you spill a bit of water on a table, you know what it is but others may not, and they must assume it is dangerous.

Waste Disposal

Relatively few substances can be disposed of in the trash or down the drain without any pretreatment. Additionally, some substances are toxic and cannot be disposed of in the trash or down the drain at all because of the potential harm they pose to the environment. Your instructor will furnish you with proper waste disposal procedures for each experiment. Follow these procedures very strictly, and do not put the environment at risk by inappropriate disposal or cleanup methods.

Percent Difference Calculation

Several of the experiments in this book require you to calculate a "percent difference." *Percent difference* is our term for the calculation commonly called "experimental error." The following is an explanation of why we prefer the different term and how to perform the calculation.

One of the conventional calculations in high school science is the so-called "experimental error." Experimental error is typically defined as the difference between the predicted value (which comes from scientific theory) and the experimental value, expressed as a percentage of the predicted value, or

$$\text{experimental error} = \frac{|\text{predicted value} - \text{experimental value}|}{\text{predicted value}} \times 100\%$$

Although the term "experimental error" is widely used, it is in our view a poor choice of words. When there is a mismatch between theory and experiment, the experiment may not be the source of the error. Often, it is the theory that is found wanting. This is how science advances.

It is, of course, true that at the high school level students are not generally engaged in research that is uncovering weaknesses in scientific theories. So the difference between prediction and experiment in a high school science experiment may well be due entirely to "experimental error." However, we hold that the pedagogical task here is to teach students how to think, and to encourage them to develop correct habits of thought. Thus, we encourage instructors to talk through this issue with their students. Help them understand that differences they find may well be due to experimental limitations or inaccuracies, but then encourage them to adopt a more inclusive way of describing the difference between prediction and experiment.

We now prefer to use the phrase "percent difference" to describe the value computed by the above equation. When quantitative results are compared to quantitative predictions or accepted values, students should compute the percent difference as

$$\text{percent difference} = \frac{|\text{predicted or accepted value} - \text{experimental value}|}{\text{predicted or accepted value}} \times 100\%$$

One more important comment needs to be made here. In the study of statistics, there is a calculation call the "percentage difference," in which the difference between two values is divided by their average. To avoid potential future confusion, instructors should point out the distinction between the calculation we are using here and the one arising in statistics.

Experiment 1
Identification of Substances by Physical Properties

1

Text Connections
- *General Chemistry*, Sections 2.2.3, 5.2.6, 5.3.11
- *Chemistry for Accelerated Students*, Sections 3.1.1, 3.2.6, 3.3.12

Objective

To confirm the physical properties of a known solid and liquid and to determine the physical properties of an unknown solid and liquid. Specifically, the properties studied will be solubility, density, melting point, and boiling point.

New Lab Skills Focus for Experiment 1

1. Laboratory safety practices
2. Use of melting point apparatus
3. Use of boiling point apparatus
4. General familiarization with laboratory apparatus

Apparatus

balance
beaker, 250 mL (2)
boiling chips
Bunsen burner and hose
capillary tubes (5)
clamp, 3-finger, with ring stand clamp*
dropper
glass stirring rod
glass tubing, 6 mm, with right-angle bend
graduated cylinder, 10 mL (4)
latex tubing, 3/16-inch ID

ring stand and 3" iron burner ring
rubber bands, small
scoopula
test tube, 25 mm × 150 mm (2)
test tube, small (12)
test tube rack
test tube stopper, #000 (12)
thermometer
two-hole stopper, No. 4 (2)
watch glass, small (2)
wire gauze

* Separate 3-finger clamp and clamp holder may be substituted for the 3-finger clamp with a built-in ring stand clamp.

Chemicals

acetone
cyclohexane
ethyl alcohol

lauric acid
unknown liquid
unknown solid

Safety

Always follow the general safety practices described in the Preface for Students. In particular, the following safety precautions should be taken during this experiment:

1. Wear nitrile gloves whenever handling any substances.
2. Wear appropriate laboratory eye protection at all times.
3. Wear a laboratory apron to protect your clothing.
4. Acetone is highly flammable. Be sure to keep the acetone away from the burner flame at all times. Treat unknown substances as if they were flammable.

Background

Often the properties of a substance allow us to determine the identity of the substance based upon physical or chemical examination. For instance, suppose you examine a metallic substance and find it has a silvery, shiny appearance like many metals. You also note that this metal is lightweight, durable, malleable, and ductile. Suppose also that you determine that this metal conducts heat and electricity well. These physical characteristics narrow the range of possibilities for the identity of the substance. Upon further examination, you discover that this metal is insoluble in water, has a density of 2.70 g/mL, and has a melting point of 660°C. Thankfully, scientists have compiled data relating to physical properties of elements and compounds and this information is readily available to us. If you refer to one of these references, you would be able to say with confidence that your substance is aluminum.

In this experiment you will examine the following physical properties of known and unknown substances: solubility, density, melting point, and boiling point. Upon the conclusion of the experiment, you will be able to confirm the identity of two known substances and determine the identity of an unknown solid substance and an unknown liquid substance.

The two known substances you are confirming, one solid and one liquid, are lauric acid and acetone. In the procedure that follows these substances are referred to as the "known substances."

Procedure

Part 1: Solubility

Each of the four substances (two known, two unknown) will be added to three different solvents to determine solubility. If the substance dissolves completely, the substance is soluble (*s*), if the substance does not dissolve (remains solid or produces cloudiness) it is insoluble (*i*). A substance may also be sparingly soluble (*sp*).

Prepare a data table in your lab journal for recording solubility data. You have three different solvents and four different solutes. Your table should allow you to record the solubility of each solute in each of the solvents.

1. Obtain three clean, dry small test tubes. Add about 2 mL of water to the first tube, add about 2 mL of cyclohexane to the second tube, and about 2 mL ethyl alcohol to the third tube.
2. Add a small scoop of lauric acid to each tube. It is not necessary to measure the solute or solvent.
3. Stopper the top of each tube and shake for 5–10 seconds.
4. Record the solubility of this substance in your data table using the abbreviations *s*—soluble, *i*—insoluble, and *sp*—sparingly soluble.
5. Repeat this procedure for the remaining three substances. For liquid substances, use a clean dropper to add 4–5 drops into each solvent.

Part 2: Density

Prepare a data table in your lab journal for recording the data needed to calculate the density of each of the two solid substances you are working with. These data include the mass, initial volume, final volume, and net volume for each solid.

To determine the density of the solid substances:

1. Weigh about 1.5 g of lauric acid to the nearest 0.01 g or better and record the mass.
2. Obtain a clean, dry 10-mL graduated cylinder and add about 5 mL of the solvent in which this solid (lauric acid) was insoluble. Record the volume to the nearest 0.1 mL.

3. Add the solid lauric acid to the graduated cylinder, being careful to ensure that all the sample goes in the solvent and not on the sides of the cylinder. Record the new volume. The difference in volume readings equals the volume of the solid.
4. Calculate the density.
5. Repeat the same procedure for the unknown solid.

   Prepare a data table in your lab journal for recording the data needed to calculate the density of each of the two liquid substances you are working with. These data include the volume, initial mass of cylinder, final mass of cylinder, and net mass of liquid for each liquid.
   To determine the density of liquid substances:

1. Obtain a clean, dry 10-mL graduated cylinder and weigh it to the nearest 0.01 g or better. Record the mass.
2. Drop about 5 mL of acetone into the graduated cylinder. Record the volume to the nearest 0.1 mL. Weigh the cylinder and record the new mass. The difference in mass equals the mass of the liquid.
3. Calculate the density.
4. Repeat the same procedure for the unknown liquid.
5. Save the liquid samples for boiling point determination (Part 4).

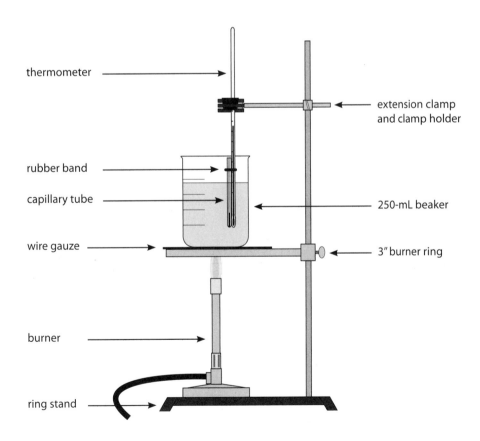

Figure 1-1. Melting point apparatus.

Part 3: Melting point of solid substances

   Familiarize yourself with the melting point apparatus shown in Figure 1-1 before proceeding. Prepare a data table in your lab journal for recording melting point data. You will need to record the melting point range determined in each of two trials for the two solid substances.

1. Pulverize a small sample of lauric acid in a watch glass.
2. Fill approximately 5 mm of your sample into the open end of the glass capillary tube by tapping the open end on the sample in the watch glass.
3. Gently tap the closed end of the capillary tube on the surface of your work bench until all the sample has reached the bottom of the tube. Alternatively, the tube can be dropped through a "glass rod" to compact the sample. (Note: A "glass rod," as they are commonly called, is a hollow glass tube about 18 inches in length that is used for compacting substances in capillary tubes.)
4. Secure the capillary tube to the thermometer using a rubber band as shown in Figure 1-1.
5. Fit the thermometer into the rubber stopper and clamp it to the ring stand.
6. Place the thermometer with capillary tube into the beaker of water. Make sure the entire sample in the capillary tube is covered by the water and the open end of the tube is above the water.
7. Ignite the Bunsen burner, adjust it to produce a moderate flame, and place it under the beaker on the ring stand. Occasionally stir the water using a stirring rod.
8. Record the temperature when the sample begins to melt. Also record the temperature when the entire sample has melted. These two temperature measurements indicate the melting-

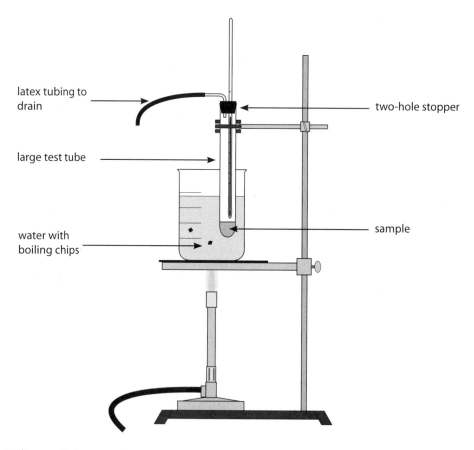

Figure 1-2. Boiling point apparatus.

point range.

9. Repeat this procedure to confirm the melting-point range. Continue to repeat until temperature ranges differ by 1°C or less.

10. Repeat the same procedure for the unknown solid.

Part 4: Boiling point of liquid substances

Familiarize yourself with the boiling point apparatus shown in Figure 1-2 before proceeding. Prepare a data table in your lab journal for recording boiling point data. You will need to record the boiling point determined in each of two trials for the two liquid substances.

1. Add about 3 mL of acetone from the sample used to calculate density (Part 2) into a clean, dry, large test tube.

2. Insert a two-hole rubber stopper into the test tube. Insert the thermometer making sure the bulb of the thermometer rests about 1 cm above the sample. Also insert a right-angle-bend glass tube connected to latex tubing. The latex tubing should be long enough to reach the sink.

3. Add two small boiling chips to the water in the beaker.

4. Position the tube in the water, making sure that the sample is submerged. Clamp the tube to the ring stand.

5. Ignite the Bunsen burner, adjust it to produce a moderate flame, and place it under the beaker on the ring stand. Watch for changes in the temperature.

6. The temperature will be constant once the sample boiling point is reached. Record the temperature.

7. Repeat this experiment to confirm the sample boiling point. Continue to repeat until temperature differs by 1°C or less.

8. Repeat steps 1–7 for the unknown liquid.

Substance	Density (g/mL)	Melting point (°C)	Boiling point (°C)	Solubility in water	Solubility in cyclohexane	Solubility in ethyl alcohol
acetone	0.79	−95	56	s	s	s
benzoic acid	1.27	122	249	i	i	s
bromoform	2.89	8	125	i	s	s
cadmium nitrate · 4H$_2$O	2.46	59	132	s	i	s
cyclohexane	0.78	6.5	81.4	i	s	s
diphenylamine	1.16	53	302	i	s	s
ether, ethyl propyl	1.37	−79	64	s	s	s
hexane	0.66	−94	69	i	s	s
isopropyl alcohol	0.79	−98	83	s	i	s
lauric acid	0.88	43	225	i	s	s
methyl alcohol	0.79	−98	65	s	i	s
naphthalene	1.15	80	218	i	s	sp
phenyl benzoate	1.23	71	314	i	s	s
stearic acid	0.85	70	291	i	s	sp
toluene	0.87	−95	111	i	s	s

Table 1-1. Physical properties of pure substances.

Analysis

Using your data and the information in Table 1-1, identify the two unknown substances. Record the identities of these substances in your lab journal.

To begin your analysis, calculate the percent difference[1] for your two known substances for density, melting point, and boiling point. Record these values in your lab journal. In your discussion, refer to these values to help establish the accuracy in your measurements and the validity of your identifications of the unknown substances.

---

1   See the Preface for Students for an explanation of this term and the calculation involved.

Experiment 1: Identification of Substances by Physical Properties
Short Form Report Sheet

Your Name	

   Your instructor will determine whether you will write a complete lab report for this experiment or use the following short form report sheet.

Part 1: Solubility

   (Show your data table here.)

Part 2: Density

   (Show your data table here.)

Part 3: Melting point of solids

(Show your data table here.)

Part 4: Boiling point of liquids

(Show your data table here.)

Unknown Identification

unknown solid	
unknown liquid	

Your Name	

Questions

1. Is bromoform a solid or liquid at room temperature?

2. What solvent would you use to measure the density of naphthalene?

3. If air bubbles were trapped in a sample of naphthalene during your volume measurement to calculate density, what error would result and how would that effect your density calculation?

4. A liquid was found to be insoluble in cyclohexane and had a density of 0.79. List the possible identities of this substance. What experiment could be performed to confirm the identity?

5. Osmium is the densest element known. Use the internet to research the physical properties of osmium. List the properties and their associated values. Additionally, specify your source.

Experiment 2
Separation of Components in a Mixture

2

Text Connections
- *General Chemistry*, Sections 2.2.3, 5.2.6, 5.3.11
- *Chemistry for Accelerated Students*, Sections 3.1.1, 3.2.6, 3.3.12

Objective

To relate knowledge of chemical and physical properties to the task of purifying a mixture. Additionally, to become familiar with decantation, vacuum filtration, evaporation, and recrystallization purification techniques.

New Lab Skills Focus for Experiment 2

1. Liquid decantation
2. Vacuum filtration (see Notes to Instructors)

Apparatus

balance
beaker, 250 mL (2)
Büchner funnel
Büchner funnel stopper
Bunsen burner and hose
clamp, 3-finger, with ring stand clamp
evaporating dish
filter paper (appropriate size to fit Büchner funnel)
glass stirring rod
graduated cylinder, 50 mL

hot plate
ring stand
spatula
tongs
vacuum flask
vacuum hose
wash bottle with distilled water (cold)
watch glass
weigh boat
wire gauze

Chemicals

benzoic acid
silicon dioxide (sand)

sodium chloride

Safety

Always follow the general safety practices described in the Preface for Students. In particular, the following safety precautions should be taken during this experiment:

1. Wear nitrile gloves whenever handling any substances.
2. Wear hot gloves when handling hot substances and apparatus.
3. Wear appropriate laboratory eye protection at all times.
4. Wear a laboratory apron to protect your clothing.

Background

Mixtures that have a uniform composition throughout—all the way down to the molecular level—are homogeneous mixtures. In a homogeneous mixture, the properties of the mixture are the same for any sample. By contrast, heterogeneous mixtures do not have a uniform composition. A small sample from one part of the mixture may have different properties from a sample taken from another part of the mixture. All mixtures are formed when substances are physically

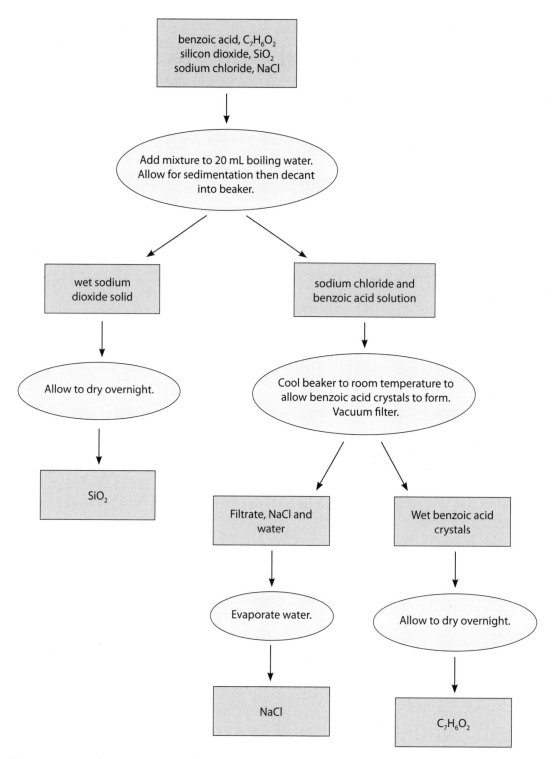

Figure 2-1. Purification process flow diagram.

combined without combining chemically. Since substances in mixtures are combined physically but not chemically, they can be separated by physical means; chemical reactions are not required.

The goal of this experiment is to separate three different substances in a heterogeneous mixture. Although the mixture may not look heterogeneous at first glance, it definitely is. (It is composed of large grains of pure substances mixed together.) The three substances are benzoic acid, silicon dioxide (sand), and sodium chloride. Knowing the physical properties of each substance enables us to devise a plan to separate the substances. For example, sodium chloride is soluble in water, silicon dioxide is not, and benzoic acid is only soluble in very hot water (near boiling). This information will guide our strategy for separation.

Additionally, we will need to employ several different purification methods to accomplish this task. These include:

1. *Decantation*—Separation of a liquid from a solid by gently pouring the liquid from a container while the solid is at rest at the bottom of the container.
2. *Vacuum filtration*—Separation of a solid from a liquid with a filter that allows only passage of the liquid substance. The vacuum aids in speeding the process along. If a vacuum is not available, gravitational filtration may also be used to accomplish the same goal.
3. *Evaporation*—The evaporation of a liquid while a solid remains behind in the container.
4. *Recrystallization*—The crystal precipitation of a pure substance.

The flow diagram in Figure 2-1 illustrates the overall separation process for this experiment.

Procedure

Prepare a data table in your lab journal for recording masses. The first two masses in your table will be the mass of the dry beaker and the mass of the beaker with mixture. The difference between these masses is the mass of your mixture, which you will enter into the same table. You will determine the masses of each of the three components in the mixture using this same method of measuring the mass of an empty container (or dish), measuring the mass again after water has evaporated off, and using the difference as the mass of the substance you have isolated. Thus, in your table you will have two measurements and a difference value for each of four difference quantities (the mixture and the three isolated components). Naturally, we would expect that when you complete the procedure, the three component masses should add up to the original mixture mass you started with. (At least, the sum should match the original mass to within the experimental uncertainty present in the measurements you make.)

Your instructor will provide you with the mass percentages for each of the three components in the mixture. Record these in your lab journal.

1. Obtain a clean, dry 250-mL beaker and determine its mass to the nearest 0.01 g or better.
2. With the beaker still on the balance, add approximately 5 g of the mixture into the beaker and record the new mass. Make sure to shake the mixture before scooping it out to ensure it is mixed well.
3. Obtain the proper gloves to handle hot objects. Add 20 mL of hot (nearly boiling) water to the beaker and swirl the beaker to dissolve components. The silicon dioxide will not dissolve, but the sodium chloride and benzoic acid are readily soluble. If traces of sodium chloride and benzoic acid are still present, add a small amount of hot water until they are fully dissolved.
4. Allow for sedimentation of the silicon dioxide to occur by letting the beaker rest on the bench top for a short time (1–2 minutes). Do not let the solution cool. If more time is necessary, let the beaker sit on a warm hot plate, but do not let solution boil.
5. Decant the sodium chloride and benzoic acid solution off the silicon dioxide as shown in the diagram in Figure 2-2. Use a glass stirring rod to guide the solution into a clean, dry, empty beaker. Decant as much liquid as possible without allowing any solid to escape the beaker.
6. Rinse the silicon dioxide with about 2 mL of hot water, allow the sediment to settle, and decant the rinse into the beaker with the sodium chloride and benzoic acid solution. Repeat

one more time for a total of two rinses.

7. Record the mass of a clean, dry watch glass. Scrape the wet silicon dioxide onto the watch glass with a spatula and allow to dry overnight in the fume hood or on the bench top.

8. Allow the beaker containing the sodium chloride and benzoic acid solution to come to room temperature. Benzoic acid crystals should become visible.

9. Set up the vacuum filtration apparatus, as shown in Figure 2-3. Turn on the vacuum. Add a few milliliters of cold distilled water to the filter paper to prime the filter. Pour the sodium chloride and benzoic acid solution into the Büchner funnel. Rinse the beaker with room temperature or cold distilled water and add to the Büchner funnel again.

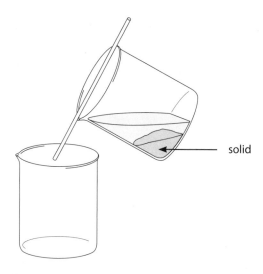

solid

Figure 2-2. Decantation of a liquid.

10. Record the mass of a second clean, dry watch glass. Scrape the benzoic acid crystals onto the watch glass and allow them to dry overnight in the fume hood or on the bench top.

11. Record the mass of a clean, dry evaporation dish. Pour the filtrate from the vacuum filtration into the evaporating dish.

12. Set up the evaporating dish on a wire gauze, burner ring, and ring stand with Bunsen burner. Ignite the Bunsen burner and gently evaporate the water from the sodium chloride.

13. Once the water has evaporated, turn off the Bunsen burner and transfer the evaporating dish to the fume hood or bench top with tongs. Allow the dish sit overnight.

14. The next day, determine the mass of the silicon dioxide and watch glass, the benzoic acid and watch glass, and the sodium chloride and evaporation dish.

15. Place a weigh boat on the balance and zero the balance. Scrape each of the recovered components into the weigh boat and record the mass of the recovered and recombined mixture.

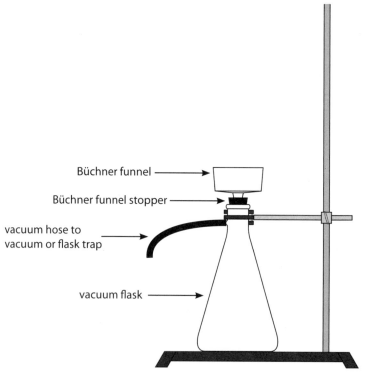

Büchner funnel

Büchner funnel stopper

vacuum hose to
vacuum or flask trap

vacuum flask

Figure 2-3. Vacuum filtration.

Analysis

Calculate the percent recovery for the mixture as

$$\text{percent recovery} = \frac{\text{original mixture mass} - \text{sum of 3 recovered component masses}}{\text{original mixture mass}} \times 100\%$$

Calculate the empirical percentages of each recovered component using your empirical component masses and the recovered mixture mass. Also calculate the percent difference[1] for each component. Use the mass percentages of your original mixture preparation as the predicted values and your empirical percentages as the experimental values.

---

1   See the Preface for Students for an explanation of this term and the calculation involved.

Experiment 2: Separation of Components in a Mixture
Short Form Report Sheet

Your Name	

Your instructor will determine whether you will write a complete lab report for this experiment or use the following short form report sheet.

In the space below show your data table, including the net mass of your original mixture and the three isolated substances.

Questions

1. Add the masses of the three components. Calculate the percent recovery for the total mixture.

2. Using your own data, calculate the percentage, by mass, of each component present in the mixture.

3. Calculate the percent difference for each component.

4. What is the interesting property of benzoic acid that enabled its separation?

5. Why was the silicon dioxide rinsed twice? How would the percent recovery of silicon dioxide be altered if it was not rinsed, or if it was rinsed with cold water?

Your Name	

6. Describe two possible tests you could use to confirm the purity of the three components you isolated. (Think again of your work in Experiment 1.) If you obtained pure substances, what values would you observe with these tests?

Experiment 3
Flame Tests and Metal Cation Identification

3

Text Connections
- *General Chemistry*, Sections 3.1.1, 3.1.2, 3.3.3
- *Chemistry for Accelerated Students*, Sections 1.1.1, 1.1.2, 1.3.3

Objective

To relate the emission spectra of a specific metal cation to its chemical identity and to use this knowledge to identify an unknown metal cation in a solution.

New Lab Skills Focus for Experiment 3

1. Handling strong acids
2. Flame tests

Apparatus

beaker, 100 mL
Bunsen burner and gas hose
nichrome or platinum wire with loop

test tubes, small (13)
test tube rack

Chemicals

distilled water
HCl, 1.0 M
0.5 M solutions of LiCl, NaCl, $MgCl_2$, KCl,

$CaCl_2$, RbCl, $SrCl_2$, CsCl, $BaCl_2$, $CuCl_2$, $ZnCl_2$, unidentified solution

Safety

Always follow the general safety practices described in the Preface for Students. In particular, the following safety precautions should be taken during this experiment:

1. Wear nitrile gloves whenever handling any substances.
2. Wear hot gloves when handling hot substances and apparatus.
3. Wear appropriate laboratory eye protection at all times.
4. Wear a laboratory apron to protect your clothing.

Background

The flame test is a qualitative method used in analytical chemistry to characterize and identify specific metal ions in solution. Metal ions emit specific wavelengths of light upon excitation. In this experiment you will characterize the color produced by metal ions and use this knowledge to identify an unknown metal ion in a solution.

Procedure

1. Make a table in your lab journal. In the left column list the 12 compounds being tested (11 known compounds and one unknown compound). Add three more columns for recording the colors you observe during three trials for each compound.
2. Obtain a test tube rack containing the 11 samples, the unknown sample, and 1.0 M HCl in

individual labeled test tubes.

3. Add 20–30 mL of distilled water into a clean 100-mL beaker.

4. Ignite the Bunsen burner.

5. Clean the wire loop as follows: dip the loop into the 1.0 M HCl solution, dip into the beaker with water, put the loop over the flame. There should be no distinguishable color rising from the loop. If there is, rinse it again.

6. Dip the loop into the first sample and place it over the hottest part of the flame, typically above the inner blue cone. As specifically and descriptively as possible, record in your lab journal the color that is emitted. Repeat this a total of three times per sample. It is not necessary to perform an HCl wash when repeating tests with the same sample, but it is necessary to wash the wire loop in the HCl solution before beginning tests on a new sample.

7. Repeat step 6 for the remaining samples.

8. After performing the flame test on the sample of unidentified solution, use your color data to identify the metal cation in the unidentified solution.

Experiment 3: Flame Tests and Metal Cation Identification
Short Form Report Sheet

Your Name	

Your instructor will determine whether you will write a complete lab report for this experiment or use the following short form report sheet.

In the space below show your data table listing the 12 samples and the colors observed during the three trials of each sample.

In the space below, identify the metal cations in the sample of unidentified solution.

Questions

1. Is there any way to relate the observed emission to the metal's location in the Periodic Table of the Elements and the number of valence electrons?

2. Every metal produces a characteristic glow when burned. Will a flame test always allow a positive identification of the presence of a particular metal? Explain why or why not.

3. Explain how light of a specific wavelength is produced by a heated metal.

Experiment 4
Determining the Empirical Formula of a
Copper Chloride Hydrate

4

Text Connections
- *General Chemistry*, Sections 3.5.1, 3.5.2
- *Chemistry for Accelerated Students*, Sections 1.5.7, 1.5.8

Objective

To determine the empirical formula for the compound $Cu_xCl_y\cdot(H_2O)_z$ by ascertaining the mole amounts of each element present in the compound.

New Lab Skills Focus for Experiment 4

Use of a crucible

Apparatus

balance	glass stirring rod
beaker, 100 mL	ring stand
Büchner funnel	scoopula
Büchner funnel stopper	tongs
Bunsen burner and hose	vacuum flask
clamp, 3-finger, with ring stand clamp	vacuum hose
clay triangle	wash bottle with distilled water
crucible	watch glass
crucible tongs	
filter paper (appropriate size to fit Büchner funnel)	

Chemicals

copper chloride hydrate	HCl, 6.0 M
distilled water	mossy zinc

Safety

Always follow the general safety practices described in the Preface for Students. In particular, the following safety precautions should be taken during this experiment:

1. Wear nitrile gloves whenever handling any substances.
2. Wear hot gloves when handling hot substances and apparatus.
3. Wear appropriate laboratory eye protection at all times.
4. Wear a laboratory apron to protect your clothing.
5. This experiment involves concentrated hydrochloric acid, a very corrosive substance. Be very careful when handling the HCl. When pouring, pour slowly to avoid a sudden release of heat. Always pour acid into water, and never the other way around.

Background

The purpose of this experiment is to determine the empirical formula for the compound: $Cu_xCl_y\cdot(H_2O)_z$. This particular compound is a hydrate, which means that water has crystallized along with the metal compound in specific ratios. This experiment begins with determining the amount of water contained in this compound by evaporating the water.

$$Cu_xCl_y \cdot (H_2O)_z\,(s) + \text{heat} \rightarrow Cu_xCl_y\,(s) + ZH_2O\,(g)$$

Next, the amount of copper will be determined by performing a single-replacement reaction with solid zinc.

$$Cu_xCl_y\,(aq) + Zn\,(s) \rightarrow XCu\,(s) + YZnCl_2\,(aq)$$

These two procedures will provide the mass of water and the mass of copper. The difference between the sum of these masses and the original sample mass will provide the mass of chlorine. The mass values obtained for each substance will allow you to calculate the mole amounts and thus determine the simplest mole ratios of copper, chlorine, and water needed to write the empirical formula.

Procedure

1. Wash a crucible with soap and water. Do a final rinse with distilled water. Dry.
2. Place the crucible on a clay triangle supported on a ring stand. Ignite the Bunsen burner under the ring stand.
3. Adjust the flame so that the inner blue cone is at the bottom of the crucible. Heat the crucible for 3–5 minutes until it glows orange. This step is important to thoroughly clean the crucible of any excess oil from hands and any substances that may not have been removed during the wash.
4. Allow the crucible to return to room temperature. This should require about 5 minutes.
5. Using crucible tongs, weigh the crucible and record the mass. Note: Always carry the crucible over a watch glass so that if dropped it doesn't fall to the floor.
6. Add approximately 1.0 g of the copper chloride hydrate to the crucible.
7. Weigh the crucible and hydrate and record the mass to the nearest 0.01 g or better.
8. Determine the mass of the copper chloride hydrate.
9. Place the crucible on the clay triangle and gently heat the sample by holding the base of the Bunsen burner and waving the tip of the flame (not the inner blue cone) under the crucible.
10. As water escapes, the green hydrated copper chloride will turn into the brown anhydrous color. Using a scoopula, stir the sample to ensure all the green crystals turn brown.
11. Once all crystals have turned brown, heat for an additional two minutes to ensure all water has escaped.
12. Turn off the Bunsen burner and allow the crucible to return to room temperature.
13. Weigh the crucible and sample and record the mass to the nearest 0.01 g or better.
14. The difference in the masses obtained in steps 7 and 13 represents the mass of water in the sample.
15. Using the scoopula, transfer the anhydrous sample into a 100-mL beaker.
16. Rinse the crucible with approximately 5 mL of distilled water and add this water to the beaker containing the anhydrous sample. Repeat. The brown anhydrous sample should now become a blue hydrated solution. Swirl the beaker to thoroughly dissolve all the crystals.
17. Obtain approximately 0.30–0.60 g of mossy zinc. While stirring with a glass stirring rod, slowly add small pieces of mossy zinc to the hydrated solution. Stop adding zinc once you have observed that all copper has come out of solution; the color will begin to fade and no longer be blue. Do not worry if you add a little too much zinc, that will be addressed in the next step. Allow the reaction to continue for five minutes.

18. Add about 15 mL 6.0 M HCl to the solution in order to put any remaining solid zinc into solution. This reaction will produce zinc chloride and hydrogen gas. Use the glass stirring rod to dislodge any particles of copper and zinc that might be clinging together and allow the zinc to go into solution. Once the bubbling has stopped, proceed to the next step.

19. Prepare the vacuum filtration apparatus as described in Experiment 2. Weigh the filter paper being used in the Büchner funnel. Record the mass to the nearest 0.01 g or better.

20. Place the filter paper in the Büchner funnel, turn on the vacuum, and add about 5 mL distilled water to the filter paper.

21. Pour the copper-containing solution in the Büchner funnel. Rinse the beaker with distilled water and add the rinse to the funnel.

22. Rinse the copper on the filter paper with 15 mL distilled water. Repeat.

23. Allow the vacuum to dry the copper for an additional 10 minutes after the rinse.

24. Obtain a clean, dry, watch glass. Record the weight of the watch glass to the nearest 0.01 g or better.

25. Carefully transfer the filter paper and copper to the watch glass. Allow to completely dry overnight. Record the mass of the watch glass, filter paper, and copper to the nearest 0.01 g or better the next day.

26. The mass of copper can be calculated by subtracting the mass in step 25 from the mass of the filter paper and watch glass.

27. The mass of chlorine can be calculated by subtracting the mass of water and the mass of copper from the original sample amount.

Analysis

Convert the masses of the copper, chlorine, and the water in the original hydrate compound into numbers of moles. Then determine the simplest mole ratio of the two elements and water and the empirical formula of the original hydrate compound.

Experiment 4: Determining the Empirical Formula of a Copper Chloride Hydrate
Short Form Report Sheet

Your Name	

Your instructor will determine whether you will write a complete lab report for this experiment or use the following short form report sheet.

In the space below show your data table with all of the mass measurements made during the experiment, the net masses of the original hydrate and each of the elements and the water in the hydrate, the number of moles of each of the elements and the water in the hydrate, and the empirical formula of the hydrate.

Questions

1. Add the masses of each component. Calculate the percent recovery for the total mixture.

2. Compare your empirical formula to the correct formula obtained from your instructor. State your formula and whether it is correct. If it is not, explain where an error could have occurred.

3. Why is it so important to make sure the single replacement reaction between the solid zinc and copper chloride solution continues to completion? Likewise, why is it important to ensure the complete removal of excess zinc with HCl?

4. Five grams of pure iron react with oxygen to form a new substance with a mass of 7.15 grams. What is the empirical formula of the iron oxide compound?

Experiment 5
Activity Series

5

Text Connections
- *General Chemistry*, Section 7.2.3
- *Chemistry for Accelerated Students*, Section 5.2.3

Objective

To determine the activity series for a set of metals based upon their reactivity in chemical reactions.

New Lab Skills Focus for Experiment 5

Use of a 24-well plate

Apparatus

24-well plate (2)   test tube rack
small test tubes (6)

Chemicals

distilled water
HCl, 6.0 M
pieces, small, (7 each), of the following
   metals: calcium, copper, iron,
   magnesium, tin, zinc

solutions, 0.2 M each, of the following
   compounds in dropper bottles: $AgNO_3$,
   $Ca(NO_3)_2$, $CuSO_4$, $Fe(NO_3)_3$, $FeSO_4$,
   $Mg(NO_3)_2$, $SnCl_4$, $Zn(NO_3)_2$

Safety

   Always follow the general safety practices described in the Preface for Students. In particular, the following safety precautions should be taken during this experiment:

1. Wear nitrile gloves whenever handling any substances.
2. Wear appropriate laboratory eye protection at all times.
3. Wear a laboratory apron to protect your clothing.
4. This experiment involves concentrated hydrochloric acid, a very corrosive substance. Be very careful when handling the HCl. When pouring, pour slowly to avoid a sudden release of heat. Always pour acid into water, and never the other way around.

Background

   The activity series for a given set of elements is a representation of their relative reactivity. The more reactive an element, the more willing it will be to give up its valence electrons and react with ionic compounds to replace the metal cation in the compound. The reactivity of a metal can be determined by performing single replacement reactions between that metal and a series of ionic solutions. The results from these reactions allow us to rank the reactivity of the metal and produce an activity series. Additionally, if the metal is high on the activity series list, it will also be able to displace the hydrogen in acids to produce hydrogen gas. On the other hand, the lower a metal appears on the list, the less vigorously it will react with acids, if it reacts with acids at all.

This experiment has been designed for you to determine the order of activity for the following metals: calcium, copper, iron, magnesium, tin, and zinc. You will begin by testing their reactivity with a concentrated solution of hydrochloric acid (HCl) and recording your observations. Next, each metal will be introduced to a series of ionic compounds to determine if the metal in question is able to displace the metal found in the ionic solution. The data gathered from these reactions will allow you to construct an activity series for these metals.

Procedure

Part 1: Reaction of metals with hydrochloric acid

1. Obtain six clean test tubes and place them in a test tube rack.
2. Add 10–15 drops of 6.0 M HCl into each tube.
3. Add a small piece of calcium metal into the first tube. Observe the reaction, if any. Allow the reaction to proceed for 20 minutes. In your lab journal, record your observations (color change, formation of gas, odor, vigorousness of the reaction).
4. Add a small piece of copper into the second tube and record your observations.
5. Continue this procedure for the remaining four metals.

Part 2: Reaction of metals with ionic solutions

1. Obtain two, clean 24-well plates.
2. Position each plate so that it lies 4 rows across and 6 columns down.
3. In each well of the first column of each plate, place a small piece of calcium. Place a small piece of copper into each well of the second column. Continue this pattern for the remaining metals as illustrated in Figures 5-1 and 5-2.
4. Add 10–15 drops of 0.2 M Ca(NO$_3$)$_2$ into each well in the first row of the first plate. Observe any reaction. Allow each reaction to proceed for 20 minutes. Record your observations (color change, formation of gas, odor, vigorousness of the reaction).
5. Repeat this procedure for the remaining ionic compounds as illustrated in Figures 5-1 and 5-2.

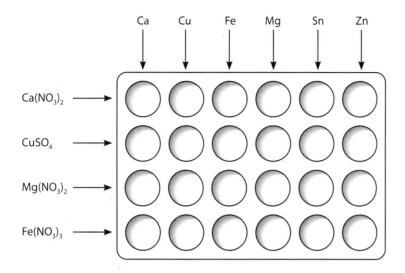

Figure 5-1. Substance arrangement for Plate 1.

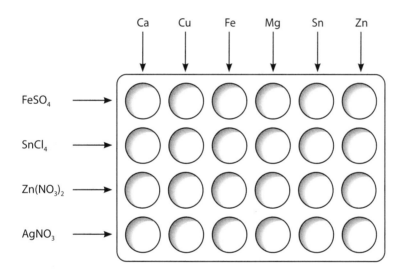

Figure 5-2. Substance arrangement for Plate 2.

Experiment 5: Activity Series
Short Form Report Sheet

Your Name	

Your instructor will determine whether you will write a complete lab report for this experiment or use the following short form report sheet.

Part 1: Reaction of metals with hydrochloric acid

In the space below indicate your observations as each of the metals reacted with hydrochloric acid. Also show the chemical equation for each reaction.

	Observations	Equation
Ca		
Cu		
Fe		
Mg		
Sn		
Zn		

Part 2: Reaction of metals with ionic solutions

Record your observations for each of the reactions below.

Solution	Metal					
	Ca	Cu	Fe	Mg	Sn	Zn
$Ca(NO_3)_2$						
$CuSO_4$						
$Mg(NO_3)_2$						
$Fe(NO_3)_3$						
$FeSO_4$						
$SnCl_4$						
$Zn(NO_3)_2$						
$AgNO_3$						

Your Name	

Write the complete equation and net ionic equation for each of the reactions listed in the table on the previous page.

Ca(NO₃)₂		
CuSO₄		
Mg(NO₃)₂		
Fe(NO₃)₃		
FeSO₄		

SnCl₄		
$SnCl_4$		
$Zn(NO_3)_2$		
$AgNO_3$		

Your Name	

Questions

1. Based upon the data, create an activity series for the metals used in this experiment.

2. How does the order of the activity series relate to valence electron count, atomic size, energy level, electron affinity, and ionization energy?

Experiment 6
Limiting Reactant and Percent Yield

Text Connections
- *General Chemistry*, Sections 7.3.2, 7.3.3
- *Chemistry for Accelerated Students*, Sections 5.3.2, 5.3.3

Objective

To determine the limiting reactant via stoichiometric calculations and to determine the percent yield of a specific product.

New Lab Skills Focus for Experiment 6

1. Gravity filtration
2. Flute folding of filter paper

Apparatus

beaker, 50 mL (2)
beaker, 250 mL (4)
beaker, 400 mL
filter funnel
filter funnel support ring (2" iron ring)
filter paper
glass stirring rod
graduated cylinder, 100 mL
hot plate

ring stand and 3" iron burner ring
rubber policeman
tape (for labeling beakers)
thermometer
tongs
wash bottle with distilled water
watch glass
weigh boats
wire gauze

Chemicals

$AgNO_3$ (solid)
distilled water
$MgCl_2$ (solid)

solutions in dropper bottles: $AgNO_3$, 0.1 M,
     $MgCl_2$, 0.2 M

Safety

Always follow the general safety practices described in the Preface for Students. In particular, the following safety precautions should be taken during this experiment:

1. Wear nitrile gloves whenever handling any substances.
2. Wear appropriate laboratory eye protection at all times.
3. Wear a laboratory apron to protect your clothing.
4. Wear hot gloves when handling hot substances and apparatus.
5. Use beaker tongs to handle hot beakers.

Background

In order to calculate the percent yield of a specific product, the limiting reactant must be identified because the limiting reactant will determine the amount of each product produced. The limiting reactant is the reactant that is completely consumed during the reaction, leaving the other reactant(s) in excess. The remainders of the other reactants are not consumed.

The double replacement reaction between aqueous silver nitrate and aqueous magnesium chloride produces soluble magnesium nitrate and insoluble silver chloride. In this experiment, you will determine the mass of specific amounts of solid silver nitrate and magnesium chloride, dissolve them into aqueous solutions, and then combine the two solutions to perform the reaction. Once the reaction is complete, you will determine the mass (actual yield) of silver chloride. Additional chemical reaction analysis of the soluble product, magnesium chloride, will allow you to determine which reactant was present in excess. You will compare your data to your stoichiometric calculations. Finally, you will calculate the percent yield of silver chloride.

To separate the silver chloride precipitate from the solution, you will use *gravity filtration* with a *flute-folded* filter paper. In the vacuum filtration used in Experiment 2, the vacuum pulls the *filtrate* (the solution liquid) through the filter. With gravity filtration, gravity alone pulls the filtrate through the filter. If there are a lot of solids, the pores in the filter can become clogged and the filtration rate can slow to a near standstill. Flute folding (described below) shapes the filter paper sort of like a coffee filter with a pointed bottom. The fluting provides a larger surface area for the filtrate to contact the filter and pass through.

Procedure

Day 1

1. Prepare about 300 mL of distilled water in a 400-mL beaker and heat on a hot plate to a temperature of around 75°C.
2. Weigh about 5 g of silver nitrate and about 1 g of magnesium chloride in separate weigh boats. Record the mass of each compound to the nearest 0.01 g or better.
3. Label one 250-mL beaker silver nitrate and another one magnesium chloride.
4. Add the solid silver nitrate and solid magnesium chloride to their respective beakers. If necessary, scrape excess compound from the weigh boat with a rubber policeman (Figure 6-1) to ensure all the compound is added to the solution.
5. Using heat-resistant gloves and/or beaker tongs, measure approximately 100 mL of warmed distilled water

Figure 6-1. A rubber policeman.

and add it to one of the beakers containing the solid compounds. Repeat for the other beaker. Swirl the beakers to dissolve the contents completely.
6. Allow the solutions to cool to room temperature.
7. While the solutions are cooling, prepare the gravity filtration apparatus.
   a. Place a piece of filter paper on a clean watch glass and determine their mass to the nearest 0.01 g or better.
   b. Flute-fold the filter paper as illustrated in Figure 6-2. Begin by folding the paper in half, and then in half again (photos 1, 2). Then fold into quarters by folding the outside edges

Figure 6-2 (opposite page). Steps for flute folding of filter paper. Preparation of the filter paper this way provides more filter surface area for the filtrate (the liquid) to contact. With more filter surface area to work with, the rate at which filtrate will pass through the filter is increased.

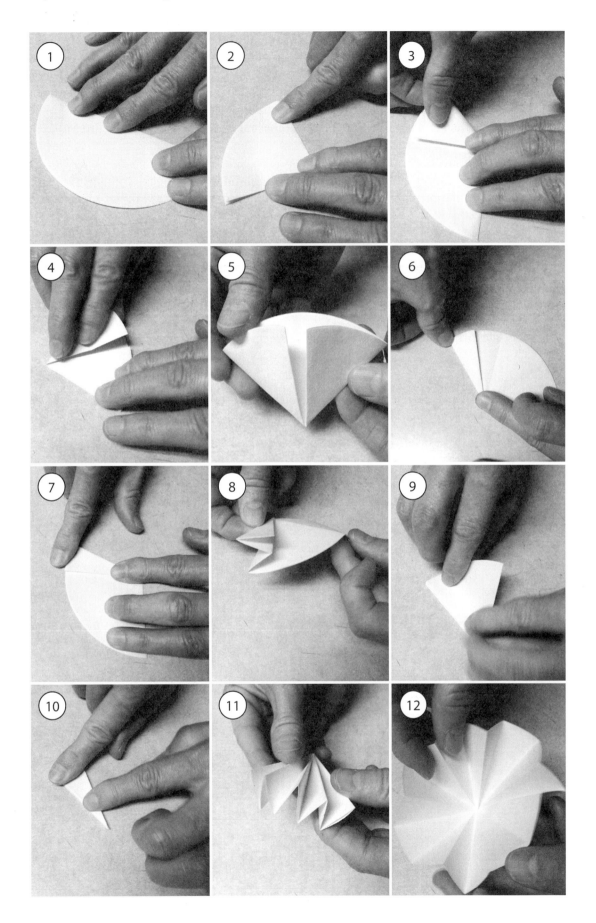

toward the center fold (photos 3, 4, 5). Then fold one of the quarter wings back toward the outside edge (photo 6). Then begin repeatedly folding back and forth, fan-wise, each fold being one-eighth of the semicircle (photos 7, 8). Continue until the entire semicircle of paper has been folded into a fan (photos 9, 10, 11). Finally, open the filter paper up in the center and you have a fluted filter paper (photo 12).

    c. Place the fluted filter paper in the glass funnel and place the funnel in the iron ring attached to the ring stand.

    d. Place a 250-mL beaker under the funnel.

8. Once the silver nitrate and magnesium chloride solutions have cooled, combine the solutions by pouring the magnesium chloride solution into the beaker with the silver nitrate solution. Record your observations.

9. Gently stir the contents of the beaker and pour the contents into the filter paper in the funnel. Use small amounts of distilled water to rinse the beaker into the filter paper. Allow the solution to drip through the filter. Once all the solution has passed through, allow the filter paper with the precipitate to dry overnight on the watch glass from step 7 (a).

10. Obtain two 50-mL beakers and place 10 mL of filtrate in each beaker. Add 10 drops of 0.2 M $MgCl_2$ to one beaker and 10 drops of 0.1 M $AgNO_3$ to the other beaker. Observe if a white precipitate forms and determine the limiting reactant from this observation.

Day 2

11. Determine the mass of the filter paper and watch glass to the nearest 0.01 g or better. Determine the mass of product formed by subtracting this value from the value obtained in step 7 (a).

Experiment 6: Limiting Reactant and Percent Yield
Short Form Report Sheet

Your Name	

Your instructor will determine whether you will write a complete lab report for this experiment or use the following short form report sheet.

In the space below, show your data table listing all of the masses taken during the procedure and the calculated mass of the precipitate.

Questions

1. Write the balanced equation for the reaction between silver nitrate and magnesium chloride. Include the states of each compound.

2. Determine the number of moles of each reactant.

3. Based upon these calculations, determine the limiting reactant. Do these stoichiometric calculations concur with your limiting reactant observation in step 10 of the procedure? Explain.

4. Determine the theoretical yield of silver chloride.

5. Calculate the percent yield of silver chloride

Experiment 7
Intermolecular Forces

7

Text Connections
- *General Chemistry*, Sections 3.1.1, 3.1.2, 3.3.3, 8.2.8
- *Chemistry for Accelerated Students*, Sections 1.1.1, 1.1.2, 1.3.3, 6.2.8

Objective

To measure the properties of six different liquids in order to characterize the type of intermolecular force that exists between the molecules of each fluid, and compare the empirical assessments to predictions based on Lewis structures and VSEPR models.

New Lab Skills Focus for Experiment 7

Assessing evaporation rate

Apparatus

beaker, 250 mL
B-Bs or small marbles (6)
boiling chips
Bunsen burner and hose
clamp, 3-finger, with ring stand clamp
filter paper
glass tubing, 6 mm, with right-angle bend
graduated cylinder, 100 mL (6)
latex tubing, 3/16-inch ID
molecular modeling kit[1]

ring stand and 3" iron burner ring
rubber bands, small
stopwatch
tape
test tube, 25 mm × 150 mm (4)
test tube rack
thermometer (4)
two-hole stopper, No. 4 (4)
wire gauze

Chemicals

acetone
ethanol
glycerol

hexane
mineral oil
water

Safety

Always follow the general safety practices described in the Preface for Students. In particular, the following safety precautions should be taken during this experiment:

1. Wear nitrile gloves whenever handling any substances.
2. Wear appropriate laboratory eye protection at all times.
3. Wear a laboratory apron to protect your clothing.
4. Wear hot gloves when handling hot substances and apparatus.
5. Use beaker tongs to handle hot beakers.

---

[1] The number AP5452 or AP6250 kits available from Flinn Scientific are suitable.

Background

Intermolecular forces, the forces between molecules, are generally weaker than the bonds between atoms that hold a molecule together. The type of intermolecular force present between molecules can be characterized by analysis of the three dimensional structure of the molecule, the polarity of the molecule, and certain physical properties such as melting point, boiling point, evaporation rate, and density. There are four different intermolecular forces: hydrogen bonding, dipole-dipole (Keesom) forces, Debye forces, and London dispersion forces.

Hydrogen bonding occurs between a hydrogen atom in a molecule and the valence electron on an oxygen, fluorine, or nitrogen atom on another molecule. This attraction occurs due to the partial positive charge of the hydrogen within the polar molecule and the highly electronegative pull of an O, F, or N atom on the electrons in the other molecule. A common example is the hydrogen bonding present between water molecules. By itself, the intermolecular force of a single hydrogen bond is weak. However, when present in large supply the cumulative intermolecular force is quite strong and is manifest in the melting point, boiling point, solubility, and viscosity for many compounds.

The other three intermolecular forces are collectively known as Van der Waals forces. Dipole-dipole (Keesom) forces are electrostatic interactions between molecules of polar-covalent compounds. Each molecule in a polar-covalent compound is a permanent dipole with $\delta+$ and $\delta-$ regions. The strength of dipole-dipole interactions follows Coulomb's Law, which states that the electrostatic force depends on the strength of all the charges and the distance between them.

Debye forces are forces between molecules that are permanent dipoles in a polar-covalent compound, and induced dipoles in the molecules of nonpolar compounds. As molecules move around, the electric field around a permanent dipole can attract or repel the electrons in a nearby nonpolar molecule and create a temporary polarization in the nonpolar molecule—a temporary dipole. Debye forces occur between molecules of two different substances and are generally weak. In this experiment, you will be testing to determine the strength of intermolecular forces in pure substances. Thus, the Debye force will play no role in this experiment.

Finally, London dispersion forces exist between nonpolar molecules. These forces are generally weak and depend on the random movement of electrons within molecules to form temporary dipoles. However, the larger the molecules, the greater the dispersion forces between them. The diatomic halogens exhibit this clearly. As atomic size increases, the room-temperature states of the diatomic halogens change from gas (F_2, Cl_2) to liquid (Br_2) to solid (I_2). Additionally, molecules with greater surface area (large or branched molecules) can experience greater dispersion forces simply because there are more possibilities for a temporary dipole to be created as the electrons move around in the orbitals of the molecule.

Procedure

Part 1: Polarity and intermolecular forces prediction

1. Create a table in your lab journal displaying the following: name of compound, Lewis structure, VSEPR geometry, overall polarity, type of intermolecular force.
2. Begin by drawing the Lewis structures for the following molecules: water (H_2O), hexane (C_6H_{14}), ethanol (C_2H_6O), acetone (C_3H_6O), glycerol ($C_3H_8O_3$), and mineral oil ($C_{18}H_{38}$).[1]
3. Determine the VSEPR geometry of each molecule.
4. Construct each molecule using the model sets.
5. Determine if the molecule is polar, and whether or not it will form hydrogen bonds.

---

1   You may need to look up the Lewis structures in your text or online.

6. Based on the size and polarity of each molecule, and on its ability to form hydrogen bonds, predict the type of intermolecular force that should be present between the molecules for each of the six compounds.

Part 2: Viscosity

The viscosity of these molecules will be determined by measuring the amount of time it takes a marble or B-B to drop down a graduated cylinder filled with a specific liquid.

1. Fill 100-mL graduated cylinders with 100 mL of each of the six compounds listed above.
2. For each cylinder, drop a marble or B-B into the cylinder of liquid from the same height. Use a stopwatch to measure the time it takes to reach the bottom. Repeat the drop three times for each of the six liquids.
3. Using your time data, develop a relative rating scale for the viscosities of the six liquids. Assign a value of 1 to the least viscous fluid and higher values for the other fluids based on the length of time required for the marble or B-B to pass through the liquid.
4. Create a bar chart showing a vertical bar for each liquid, with the heights of the bar indicating the relative viscosities.

Part 3: Boiling point

Prepare a boiling point apparatus as shown in Figure 1-2 of Experiment 1 in order to determine the boiling points for water, hexane, ethanol, and acetone. Glycerol and mineral oil will not be tested due to the very high boiling points of these substances.

1. Add about 3 mL of water into a clean, dry, large test tube.
2. Insert a two-hole rubber stopper in the test tube. Insert the thermometer, making sure the bulb of the thermometer rests about 1 cm above the sample. Also insert a right-angle-bend glass tube connected to latex tubing. The latex tubing should be long enough to reach the sink.
3. Position the test tube in the water making sure that the sample is submerged. Clamp the tube to the ring stand.
4. Ignite the Bunsen burner and watch for changes in the temperature.
5. The temperature will be constant once the boiling point is reached. Record the temperature.
6. Repeat this experiment to confirm the boiling point. Continue to repeat until temperature differs by 1°C or less.
7. Repeat the same procedure for hexane, ethanol, and acetone.
8. Rate each substance from lowest boiling point to highest boiling point.

Part 4: Evaporation

The evaporation rate will be determined by calculating the change in temperature over a specific amount of time.

1. Obtain six pieces of filter paper. Soak each one in one of the six liquids—water, hexane, ethanol, acetone, glycerol, and mineral oil. Your papers should be soaked but not dripping.
2. Wrap each filter paper around the end of a digital thermometer and secure with a rubber band.
3. Tape the thermometers down on the bench top and allow the ends of the thermometers to hang over the sink.
4. Begin timing the experiment. Record the temperature at time 0 and repeat every 30 seconds for 10 minutes.
5. Using your temperature and time data, develop a relative rating scale for the evaporation

rate of the six liquids. Assign a value of 1 to the fluid that evaporates the slowest and higher values for the other fluids based on how fast the temperature was observed to change.[2]

6. Create a bar chart showing a vertical bar for each liquid, with the heights of the bar indicating the relative evaporation rates.

---

2   For details on why evaporation lowers the temperature, see section 8.2.8 in *General Chemistry* or section 6.2.8 in *Chemistry for Accelerated Students*.

Experiment 7: Intermolecular Forces
Short Form Report Sheet

Your Name	

Your instructor will determine whether you will write a complete lab report for this experiment or use the following short form report sheet.

In the space below, create a table displaying all the information from Part 1, including your prediction of the type of intermolecular force the molecule should exhibit.

In the space below, create a table displaying all the data collected in the experiment. Include the relative viscosity rating, boiling point data (if applicable), and the relative evaporation rate.

Your Name	

Questions

1. Compare the viscosity ratings for the six substances. Explain how the viscosity rating should relate to the type of intermolecular forces present between the molecules.

2. Compare the boiling points for the six substances. Explain how the boiling point should relate to the type of intermolecular forces present between the molecules.

3. Compare the evaporation rate ratings for the six substances. Explain how the evaporation rate rating should relate to the type of intermolecular forces present between the molecules.

4. Use your viscosity, boiling point, and evaporation rate data to assign an empirical rating for the overall strength of the intermolecular forces present in each compound.

5. Compare your empirical intermolecular force rankings to your predictions of the intermolecular forces for the molecules. Comment in detail on how well your data support your predictions. In each case, explain why your data do or do not support your prediction.

6. Explain why the temperature of a substance changes like it does during evaporation.

Experiment 8
Molarity

8

Text Connections
- *General Chemistry*, Section 10.3.1
- *Chemistry for Accelerated Students*, Section 8.4.1

Objective

To determine the molarity of a solution using two different approaches: mass-to-mole relationships and titration data.

New Lab Skills Focus for Experiment 8

1. Gravity filtration
2. Titration

Apparatus

beaker, 250 mL (2)
buret, 25 mL
buret clamp
filter funnel (2)
filter paper

graduated cylinder, 25 mL (2)
graduated cylinder, 50 mL
ring stand
wash bottle with distilled water
watch glass

Chemicals

distilled water
iron (II) sulfate solution (unidentified molarity)
potassium permanganate solution, 0.05 *M*

silver nitrate, 0.1 *M*
sodium carbonate solution (unidentified molarity)
sulfuric acid, 3.0 *M*

Safety

Always follow the general safety practices described in the Preface for Students. In particular, the following safety precautions should be taken during this experiment:

1. Wear nitrile gloves whenever handling any substances.
2. Wear appropriate laboratory eye protection at all times.
3. Wear a laboratory apron to protect your clothing.
4. This experiment involves concentrated sulfuric acid, a very corrosive substance. Be very careful when handling the H_2SO_4. When pouring, pour slowly to avoid a sudden release of heat. Always pour acid into water, and never the other way around.

Background

The molarity of a solution is a measure of its concentration, namely, the mole amount of solute per liter of solution. The equation for calculating molarity, *M*, is

$$M = \frac{\text{amount of solute in moles}}{\text{volume of solution in liters}}$$

The molarity of a solution can be determined via stoichiometric analysis of substances in a reaction or by a quantitative technique known as titration. Titration is a useful method that allows an unknown concentration of a solution to be determined by the controlled addition of a solution with a known concentration. Once again, the stoichiometric analysis of the two solutions used in the titration allows one to determine the unknown molarity.

In Part 1 of this experiment you will analyze a reaction product, silver carbonate, which is a solid formed from the following reaction between sodium carbonate and silver nitrate solutions:

$$Na_2CO_3(aq) + 2AgNO_3(aq) \rightarrow Ag_2CO_3(s) + 2NaNO_3(aq)$$

A known concentration of silver nitrate will react with an unknown concentration of sodium carbonate. The solid silver carbonate produced by the reaction will be filtered, dried, and weighed. The mass of the silver carbonate will be used to calculate the number of moles of sodium carbonate present, and from there the molarity of the original solution.

In Part 2 you will use titration of a potassium permanganate solution of a known concentration with an iron (II) sulfate solution of an unknown concentration. This type of reaction is an oxidation-reduction (redox) reaction. In redox reactions, electrons are transferred between atoms in the reaction, resulting in a change in oxidation states for the atoms giving or accepting electrons. Sulfuric acid will be added to the reaction in order to provide the acidic conditions necessary for the reaction to occur. The overall reaction is as follows:

$$2KMnO_4(aq) + 10FeSO_4(aq) + 8H_2SO_4(aq) \rightarrow$$

$$K_2SO_4(aq) + 2MnSO_4(aq) + 5Fe_2(SO_4)_3(aq) + 8H_2O(l)$$

The 0.05 M potassium permanganate solution will be used in the buret. This solution of known concentration is called the *titrant*. The unidentified concentration of iron (II) sulfate will be determined by the slow addition of potassium permanganate from the buret. The solution of unidentified concentration is called the *analyte* or *titrand*. Potassium permanganate solution has a deep purple color. When added to iron (II) sulfate solution (slightly green in color), the reaction produces a clear solution. This is due to the reduction of the manganese in the permanganate ion. (You will explore redox reactions more thoroughly in Experiments 16, 17, and 18.) The end point of the titration has been reached once the solution is no longer colorless and maintains a pale pink color. At this point the iron (II) sulfate has completely reacted and is no longer present to react with the potassium permanganate. The volume of potassium permanganate required to completely react with the iron (II) sulfate can be used to determine the unidentified molarity of the iron (II) sulfate solution.

Procedure

Preparing Filter Paper for Gravity Filtration

As before in Experiment 6, in this experiment you will use gravity filtration. This time, instead of using flute folding you will use a more common technique of preparing the filter paper. For gravity filtration to work most efficiently, the moistened upper rim of the filter paper must adhere to the funnel all the way around the rim. To ensure this happens, the round sheets of filter paper are folded in a special way. As illustrated in Figure 8-1, first fold the paper in half. Then fold it again, but not quite in half, as indicated by the arrows in the second photo. Next, tear a notch out of the upper corner on the edge of the shorter side, as indicated by the arrow in the third photo. Finally, as shown in the fourth photo, open the filter paper into a cone with the torn corner and one more layer all on one side and a single layer of paper on the other side.

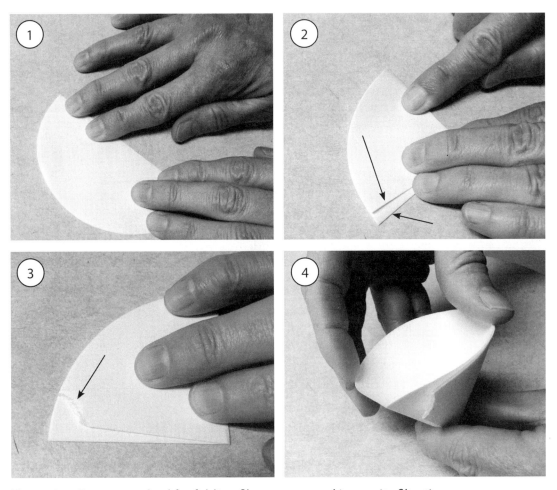

Figure 8-1. Correct method for folding filter paper used in gravity filtration.

When you place the filter paper into the glass funnel, use a wash bottle filled with distilled water to moisten the upper rim of the filter paper all the way around. The upper rim of the filter paper will then adhere to the glass all the way around the funnel. When folded as described, the angle of the filter paper cone will be slightly greater than the angle of the funnel, as shown in Figure 8-2. The upper edge of the filter is in contact with the funnel, but the rest of the filter paper hangs free, allowing for the most efficient filtration. The purpose of the notch torn on the corner of the paper is to allow the upper rim of filter paper to stretch out just a bit more, ensuring that the desired upper-rim contact occurs.

Figure 8-2. Proper folding allows the upper rim of the filter paper to contact the funnel. The rest of the paper hangs inside the funnel, allowing for the most efficient filtration.

Part 1: Determination of the molarity of the reactant based upon the mass of the product.

1.   Add about 25 mL of 0.1 *M* silver nitrate solution to a 50-mL graduated cylinder. Record the volume to the nearest 0.1 mL.
2.   Add about 15 mL of sodium carbonate to a 25-mL graduated cylinder. Record the volume to the nearest 0.1 mL.
3.   Pour both solutions into a 250-mL beaker. Record your observa-

tions. Allow the precipitate to settle to the bottom and prepare the filtration apparatus in step 4.

4. Place a filter funnel in a ring stand with a clean 250-mL beaker under the funnel. After preparing the filter paper as described in the previous section, record the mass of a piece of filter paper to the nearest 0.01 g or better. Place the filter in the funnel and moisten the filter paper around its upper rim by rinsing it with distilled water. The filter paper should now firmly adhere to the glass funnel all the way around its upper rim.

5. Pour the contents of the beaker into the filter paper. Rinse the beaker with distilled water to remove all the precipitate and pour the contents into the filter paper again. Allow the filtrate to flow into a clean beaker.

6. Gently lift the filter paper with the precipitate and place it on a watch glass to dry over night. Once dry, record the mass of the precipitate and filter paper to the nearest 0.01 g or better.

Part 2: Determination of the molarity of an unidentified solution via titration.

1. Obtain a 25-mL buret and close the valve. Fill a 25-mL buret with 0.05 *M* potassium permanganate. Record the volume to the nearest 0.1 mL. Due to the dark color of potassium permanganate, it is necessary to read the volume at the top of the meniscus instead of the bottom of the meniscus as one would normally do.

2. Add about 20 mL of iron (II) sulfate solution to a 25-mL graduated cylinder. Record the volume to the nearest 0.1 mL.

3. Pour the iron (II) sulfate into a 250-mL beaker and add about 10 mL of 3.0 *M* sulfuric acid to the beaker as well. Swirl the beaker to mix the contents and place the beaker under the buret.

4. Turn the valve on the buret to add a small amount of potassium permanganate to the beaker containing iron (II) sulfate. Gently swirl the contents of the beaker. Record any observations.

5. Repeat step 4 until the pink or purple color begins to stay longer after the beaker is swirled before fading. At this point, begin adding the potassium permanganate in very small increments. This may be done by turning the valve on the buret a full 180° in one quick motion. The amount of liquid released with each quick turn of the valve will be less than 0.5 mL. Stop adding potassium permanganate once the contents of the beaker develop a light pink or purple color that does not fade. This represents the end point of titration. Record the volume on the buret to the nearest 0.1 mL.

6. Repeat the titration procedure multiple times until you have three readings of $\Delta V = (V_f - V_i)$ from the buret that are spread over a range of no more than 0.5 mL.

Experiment 8: Molarity
Short Form Report Sheet

Your Name	

Your instructor will determine whether you will write a complete lab report for this experiment or use the following short form report sheet.

In the space below, create a table displaying all the data taken in this experiment.

Questions

Part 1

1. Based on the volume of 0.1 *M* silver nitrate you used in this reaction, calculate the theoretical yield and percent yield of silver carbonate.

2. Based on the mass of silver carbonate produced, determine the number of moles of sodium carbonate that were consumed in the reaction and the molarity of the sodium carbonate solution.

3. Calculate the molarity for sodium carbonate based on the volume of 0.1 M silver nitrate you used in this reaction. Using this value as your prediction and your molarity value from the previous question as your result, calculate the percent difference.[1] Use the percent difference to discuss the agreement between these two computations of the sodium carbonate molarity. Identify the value that is probably more accurate and explain why.

Part 2

4. Determine the average amount of potassium permanganate (ΔV) used in your titrations.

5. Based upon the average ΔV, determine the number of moles of potassium permanganate consumed in the reaction.

6. Determine the number of moles of iron (II) sulfate that were present in the reaction and the molarity of the iron (II) sulfate solution.

_____

1   See the Preface for Students for an explanation of this term and the calculation involved.

Experiment 9
Mole Amount of a Gas

9

Text Connections
- *General Chemistry*, Sections 9.3.2, 9.4.1
- *Chemistry for Accelerated Students*, Sections 7.3.2, 7.4.1

Objective

First, to determine the mole amount of a gas produced by collecting the gas over water. Second, to use stoichiometric analysis to relate the moles of gas produced to the gram amount of reactant and calculate the percent yield of gas.

New Lab Skills Focus for Experiment 9

Collection of a gas over water

Apparatus

barometer
clamp, 3-finger, with ring stand clamp
glass tubing, 6 mm, with right-angle bend
graduated cylinder, 500 mL, polypropylene
Erlenmeyer flask, 125 mL
latex tubing, 3/16-inch ID

pneumatic trough or deep plastic tray
ring stand
rubber stopper, #5½, with hole
thermometer
weigh boat, small (1 5/8 in × 1 5/8 in)

Chemicals

acetic acid, 0.1 *M*
aluminum foil

hydrochloric acid, 6.0 *M*
sodium bicarbonate

Safety

Always follow the general safety practices described in the Preface for Students. In particular, the following safety precautions should be taken during this experiment:

1. Wear nitrile gloves whenever handling any substances.
2. Wear appropriate laboratory eye protection at all times.
3. Wear a laboratory apron to protect your clothing.

Background

A common method used to determine the number of moles of gas produced during a reaction is the collection of the gas over water. This method is especially useful for gases whose solubility in water is limited. An inverted tube, in our case a graduated cylinder, filled with water is placed in a trough filled with water. One end of a latex tube is threaded inside the cylinder, while the other end of the latex tube is secured to a section of glass tubing and rubber stopper in a reaction vessel (an Erlenmeyer flask). The gas produced from the reaction is forced through the tube and displaces the water in the graduated cylinder. Once the reaction is complete, the volume of gas produced can easily be measured.

The majority of gas inside the graduated cylinder is the gas from the reaction. However, water vapor is also present, and to determine the amount of gas present we must determine the partial pressure of the gas. Dalton's law of partial pressures provides a simple calculation to determine the pressure of gas evolved from the reaction by taking into account the vapor pressure of water at a specific temperature. Vapor pressure data for water at various temperatures are shown in Table 9-1. If the water levels inside and outside of the graduated cylinder are the same, then the total pressure of the water vapor and gas system inside the cylinder is equal to the local barometric pressure, or

$$P_T = P_{atm} = P_{water\ vapor} + P_{gas}$$

Once the pressure of gas has been determined, the ideal gas law can be used to determine the number of moles of gas present:

$$PV = nRT$$

Temperature (°C)	Vapor Pressure (Torr, mm Hg)
20	17.5
21	18.7
22	19.8
23	21.1
24	22.4
25	23.8
26	25.2
27	26.7

Table 9-1. Vapor pressure of water at various temperatures.

In Part 1 of this experiment you will study the reaction between hydrochloric acid and aluminum.

$$Al(s) + HCl(aq) \rightarrow AlCl_3(aq) + H_2(g) \qquad \text{(formula equation)}$$

You will determine the amount of hydrogen produced using the method described above. Additionally, you will calculate the theoretical yield of hydrogen gas and compare it to the actual yield by calculating the percent yield of hydrogen gas.

In Part 2 you will study the well-known reaction between acetic acid (the main ingredient in vinegar other than water) and sodium bicarbonate (baking soda).

$$CH_3COOH(aq) + NaHCO_3(s) \rightarrow NaCH_3COO(aq) + H_2O(l) + CO_2(g)$$

This time, the mass of sodium bicarbonate will be unknown. The calculated mole amount of carbon dioxide gas will allow you to employ stoichiometric analysis to determine the gram amount of sodium bicarbonate. Comparison between the experimental calculation and the actual mass, known by your instructor, will allow you to determine the percent difference.

Procedure

Part 1: Percent yield of hydrogen gas

1. Prepare the apparatus for the collection of gas over water as depicted in Figure 9-1. Use the results of your pre-lab calculations (see page 65) to estimate how deeply to place the graduated cylinder in the water. When the cylinder collects an amount of gas approximately equal to your calculation, an equal volume of water will be pushed out of the cylinder, raising the level of water in the trough. Estimate where this water level will be, and adjust the graduated cylinder vertically so that the mark corresponding to your calculated volume is at this height.
2. Fill the 500-mL graduated cylinder with water to the brim. Place your hand or a glass plate over the graduated cylinder, invert the graduated cylinder so that the top of the cylinder is completely submerged in water in the trough. Carefully remove your hand or glass plate and secure the graduated cylinder with a clamp attached to a ring stand.
3. Make sure the latex tubing is inside the inverted graduated cylinder, near the top. You want

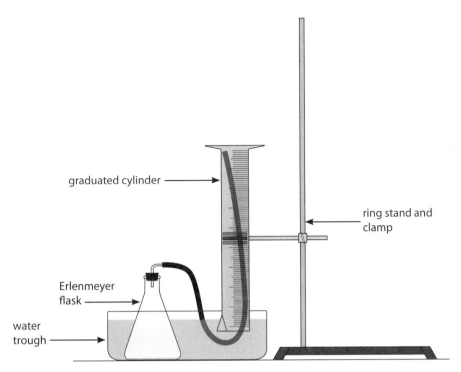

Figure 9-1. Setup for collecting gas over water.

to minimize the risk of water re-entering the tubing when the gas cools and decreases in volume.

4. Add about 10 mL of 6.0 *M* HCl to a 125-mL Erlenmeyer flask. Weigh about 0.25 g of aluminum foil and record the mass to the nearest 0.01 g or better. Add the aluminum to the HCl and immediately seal the flask with the rubber stopper connected to rubber tubing in the apparatus.

5. Swirl the flask. The reaction does not immediately occur due to the presence of oxidized aluminum on the surface of the foil (the so-called *autopassivation* layer). Once the HCl has reacted with the Al_2O_3, the reaction with aluminum will occur and H_2 gas will be produced. This reaction is exothermic, so to ensure that the temperature of the gas is the same as temperature of the water vapor, the flask must be placed in the water to bring the gas temperature to the same temperature as the water and water vapor. Since the flask will be nearly empty except for a few milliliters of HCl solution, one of the student team members will need to hold the flask firmly on the bottom of the trough after the swirling has assisted the reaction to commence.

6. Once the reaction is complete and gas production has stopped, wait until the gas produced and water have reached thermal equilibrium. Then adjust the graduated cylinder by moving it vertically until the water levels inside and outside the cylinder are the same. (This indicates that the total pressure inside the cylinder is equal to the barometric pressure in your lab.) Then record the volume of gas collected over water and the temperature of the water in the trough. The volume of H_2 gas is read using the markings on the graduated cylinder.

7. Using a barometer in the classroom, record the barometric pressure.

Part 2: Calculating the percent difference for a reactant.

1. Prepare the apparatus for the collection of gas over water, as in Part 1. Use your experience from Part 1 to judge how to position the graduated cylinder.

2. Add 30 mL of 0.1 *M* acetic acid to a clean 125-mL Erlenmeyer flask.
3. Obtain a small weigh boat of sodium bicarbonate with a mass unknown to you.
4. Carefully place the weigh boat in the flask while the flask is tilted on one side. (Bend up the sides of the boat to fit it through the neck of the flask.) Do not let the sodium bicarbonate in the weigh boat come into contact with the acetic acid.
5. Seal the flask with the rubber stopper connected to the rubber tubing and make sure the tubing extends properly up into the graduated cylinder as before.
6. Vigorously shake the flask in order to mix the sodium bicarbonate contents in the weigh boat with the acetic acid.
7. Once the reaction is complete and gas production has stopped, wait until gas produced and water have reached thermal equilibrium. Then adjust the graduated cylinder by moving it vertically until the water level inside and outside the cylinder are the same. Then record the volume of gas collected over water and the temperature of the water in the trough.
8. Using a barometer in the classroom, record the barometric pressure.

Analysis

Part 1: Percent yield of hydrogen gas

Using Dalton's law of partial pressures and your temperature and pressure data, determine the partial pressure of the hydrogen gas. Then determine the number of moles produced using the ideal gas law. Finally, calculate the percent yield of hydrogen gas. (Balance the formula equation before you perform any stoichiometry.)

Part 2: Calculate the percent difference of a reactant

As in Part 1, calculate the pressure of carbon dioxide and determine the number of moles of carbon dioxide gas produced. Then determine the mass in grams of sodium bicarbonate required to produce that mole quantity of carbon dioxide. Compare the calculated gram amount of sodium bicarbonate to the actual gram amount given by your instructor. Using your calculated value of the $NaHCO_3$ mass as the experimental value and the instructor's mass as the predicted or actual value, calculate the percent difference for the sodium bicarbonate mass.

Experiment 9: Mole Amount of a Gas
Short Form Report Sheet

Your Name	

Your instructor will determine whether you will write a complete lab report for this experiment or use the following short form report sheet.

Pre-Lab Requirement: To measure the volume of gas produced, you will adjust the graduated cylinder up and down until the water levels inside and out side the cylinder are the same. To make this possible, you need to anticipate the approximate volume of gas that will be produced by the reaction and set the cylinder in the apparatus with this volume mark slightly above the water level in the trough. As the gas collects, an equal amount of water will be pushed out of the cylinder, raising the water level in the trough. From Table 10-1 you can see that the vapor pressure of water will be about 20 Torr, which means the partial pressure of the gas produced (either one) will be around 740 Torr (since atmospheric pressure is around 760 Torr). Use this value along with the results of a stoichiometric calculation to approximate the volume of gas produced by the reaction in Part 1. (Assume room temperature, 22°C.) Use this volume to adjust the graduated cylinder properly in the apparatus.

In the spaces below show your data.

Part 1: Show your data table with the mass measurement made during the experiment, the temperature of the water, the volume of gas produced, the barometric pressure, the pressure of water vapor, the pressure of hydrogen gas, the number of moles produced, and the percent yield of hydrogen gas.

Part 2: Show your data table with the temperature of the water, the volume of gas produced, the barometric pressure, the pressure of water vapor, the pressure of carbon dioxide gas, the number of moles produced, the mass of sodium bicarbonate, and the percent difference for the sodium bicarbonate mass.

Questions and Calculations
Part 1

1. Show your calculation of the partial pressure of hydrogen gas collected over water.

2. Show your calculation of the moles of hydrogen gas produced using the ideal gas law.

3. Show your calculation of the number of moles of hydrogen gas predicted by the stoichiometry, based on the mass, volume, and concentration data for the reactants.

Your Name	

4. What is the percent yield of hydrogen gas? Explain why the theoretical yield is higher than the actual.

Part 2

5. Show your calculation of the partial pressure of carbon dioxide gas collected over water.

6. Show your calculation of the moles of carbon dioxide gas produced using the ideal gas law.

7. Show your calculation of the unknown mass of sodium bicarbonate and the percent difference between this value and the value stated by the instructor.

Experiment 10
Metathesis Reactions

10

Text Connections
• *General Chemistry*, Sections 7.2.5, 10.4.1, 10.4.2
• *Chemistry for Accelerated Students*, Sections 5.2.5, 8.5.2, 8.5.2

Objective

First, to predict precipitation and gas evolution in metathesis (double replacement) reactions of known solutions, and to identify the substances precipitated and gases evolved. Second, to use the knowledge gained to develop a strategy that will enable the identification of unknown compounds in solution.

New Lab Skills Focus for Experiment 10

Comparing precipitates

Apparatus
24-well plate (2)

Chemicals

0.1 M solutions in dropper bottles: $AgNO_3$, $Ba(NO_3)_2$, $Cu(NO_3)_2$, NaCl, Na_2CO_3, NaI, Na_2SO_4, $Pb(NO_3)_2$
2.0 M solution in dropper bottle: HNO_3

0.1 M solutions in dropper bottles (4) labeled "Unidentified Solution 1," "Unidentified Solution 2, " etc.

Safety

Always follow the general safety practices described in the Preface for Students. In particular, the following safety precautions should be taken during this experiment:

1. Wear nitrile gloves whenever handling any substances.
2. Wear appropriate laboratory eye protection at all times.
3. Wear a laboratory apron to protect your clothing.

Background

Metathesis reactions, also known as double replacement reactions, are characterized by the exchange of cations and anions in aqueous solution. These reactions can ultimately reduce the concentration of ions in solution by producing a precipitate (solid), weak electrolyte, nonelectrolyte, or gas as a product. The two types of metathesis reactions we will examine are precipitation and acid–carbonate compound reactions. These reactions are reflected in the following two general equations:

Precipitation reactions: formation of a solid

$$AX(aq) + BY(aq) \rightarrow AY(aq) + BX(s)$$

Acid–carbonate compound reactions: formation of a gas (CO$_2$(g))

$$\text{HX}(aq) + \text{BCO}_3(aq) \;\rightarrow\; \text{BX}(aq) + \text{H}_2\text{CO}_3(aq)^* \;\rightarrow\; \text{BX}(aq) + \text{H}_2\text{O}(l) + \text{CO}_2(g)$$

*H$_2$CO$_3$(aq) is an unstable acid and readily decomposes to H$_2$O(l) + CO$_2$(g).

Analysis of the net ionic equation allows us to identify the ions involved in the formation of a precipitate, water, or gas. Consider the reaction between sodium carbonate and hydrochloric acid. The complete molecular equation is as follows:

$$\text{Na}_2\text{CO}_3(aq) + 2\text{HCl}(aq) \;\rightarrow\; 2\text{NaCl}(aq) + \text{H}_2\text{O}(l) + \text{CO}_2(g)$$

For each of the compounds in aqueous solution, we write the compounds as separate aqueous ions, giving us the ionic equation:

$$2\text{Na}^+(aq) + \text{CO}_3^{2-}(aq) + 2\text{H}^+(aq) + 2\text{Cl}^-(aq) \;\rightarrow\; 2\text{Na}^+(aq) + 2\text{Cl}^-(aq) + \text{H}_2\text{O}(l) + \text{CO}_2(g)$$

Elimination of spectator ions results in the net ionic equation:

$$\text{CO}_3^{2-}(aq) + 2\text{H}^+(aq) \;\rightarrow\; \text{H}_2\text{O}(l) + \text{CO}_2(g)$$

Strong electrolytes dissociate completely in water and are thus water soluble. If the combination of two aqueous solutions produces a strong electrolyte, no reaction occurs and the ions remain in solution. Consider the reaction between sodium chloride and ammonium nitrate. The complete molecular equation is as follows:

$$\text{NaCl}(aq) + \text{NH}_4\text{NO}_3(aq) \;\rightarrow\; \text{NaNO}_3(aq) + \text{NH}_4\text{Cl}(aq)$$

Writing the aqueous compounds as separate aqueous ions gives us the ionic equation:

$$\text{Na}^+(aq) + \text{Cl}^-(aq) + \text{NH}_4^+(aq) + \text{NO}_3^-(aq) \;\rightarrow\; \text{Na}^+(aq) + \text{NO}_3^-(aq) + \text{NH}_4^+(aq) + \text{Cl}^-(aq)$$

At this point it is obvious that no ions contribute to the formation of a precipitate, water, or gas. No product remains once all the spectator ions are cancelled and thus there is no reaction:

$$\text{Na}^+(aq) + \text{Cl}^-(aq) + \text{NH}_4^+(aq) + \text{NO}_3^-(aq) \;\rightarrow\; \textit{no reaction}$$

Whether a metathesis reaction will occur can be determined by applying the solubility guidelines summarized in Table 10-1. In this experiment, you will predict the precipitations that will result from each of 16 metathesis reactions based on the information in Table 10-1. Then you will observe the 16 reactions and compare your observations to your predictions. Next, you will add 2.0 *M* nitric acid to each of the precipitates formed earlier and formulate a general rule associating the reactions between types of solids and HNO$_3$ with the formation of CO$_2$(g). Then you will devise a scheme to test a series of four unknown solutions to identify the compounds present in the solutions. Your careful observations will allow you to determine the identity of four unknown compounds chosen from the eight compounds you previously tested.

Soluble Compounds

Compounds Containing These Anions	Cations That Are Significant Exceptions
NO_3^-	None
CH_3COO^-	None
Cl^-	Compounds of Ag^+, Hg_2^{2+}, Pb^{2+}
Br^-	Compounds of Ag^+, Hg_2^{2+}, Pb^{2+}
I^-	Compounds of Ag^+, Hg_2^{2+}, Pb^{2+}
SO_4^{2-}	Compounds of Sr^{2+}, Ba^{2+}, Hg_2^{2+}, Pb^{2+}

Insoluble Compounds

Compounds Containing These Anions	Cations That Are Significant Exceptions
S^{2-}	Compounds of NH_4^+, alkali metal ions, Ca^{2+}, Sr^{2+}, Ba^{2+}
O^{2-}	Compounds of NH_4^+, alkali metal ions, Sr^{2+}, Ba^{2+}
CO_3^{2-}	Compounds of NH_4^+, alkali metal ions
PO_4^{3-}	Compounds of NH_4^+, alkali metal ions
OH^-	Compounds of NH_4^+, alkali metal ions, Ca^{2+}, Sr^{2+}, Ba^{2+}

Table 10-1. Solubility guidelines for ionic compounds in water.

Procedure

Part 1: Precipitation matrix

1. Obtain eight dropper bottles containing 0.1 M aqueous solutions of the following: $AgNO_3$, $Ba(NO_3)_2$, $Cu(NO_3)_2$, $NaCl$, Na_2CO_3, NaI, Na_2SO_4, $Pb(NO_3)_2$.
2. Add five drops of each solution to a 24-well plate according to the matrix shown in Figure 10-1 and the following description.
3. First, add five drops of 0.1 M NaCl into each well in the first column, five drops of 0.1 M NaI into each well of the second column, five drops of 0.1 M Na_2SO_4 into the third column, and five drops of 0.1 M Na_2CO_3 into each well of the fourth column.
4. Next, add solutions to the wells as follows, recording your observations in your lab journal for each one.
5. Add five drops of $Ba(NO_3)_2$ into each occupied well of the first row, five drops of $AgNO_3$ into each well of the second row, five drops of $Pb(NO_3)_2$ into each well of the third row, and five drops of $Cu(NO_3)_2$ into each well of the fourth row.

Part 2: Precipitate–nitric acid reactions

6. After recording all data for Part 1, drop 3–5 drops of 2.0 M nitric acid on each well containing a precipitate, recording your observations in each case.
7. Write the molecular and total ionic equations for the reaction with HNO_3. The precipitate from the first reaction and nitric acid are the reactants.

Part 3: Identification of unidentified solutions

8. Obtain a second clean 24-well plate and four unidentified solutions. The unidentified solutions were selected from the eight previously tested in Parts 1 and 2.
9. Based on the results of the precipitation observations, and the reactions of selected pre-

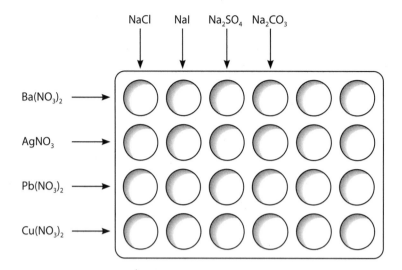

Figure 10-1. Precipitation matrix for Plate 1.

cipitates with nitric acid, design a scheme to identify the unidentified solutions using the known reagents. Then conduct your test on each of the four unidentified solutions. For each unidentified solution, record which reactions were performed and which of the following results was observed:

- no precipitate
- precipitate (what color?)
- if precipitate is present, can it be dissolved by nitric acid?

Experiment 10: Metathesis Reactions
Short Form Report Sheet

Your Name	

Your instructor will determine whether you will write a complete lab report for this experiment or use the following short form report sheet.

Part 1: Precipitation matrix

Pre-Lab Requirement: Write the complete molecular equation, complete ionic equation, and net ionic equation for each reaction performed in Part 1 (16 reactions, 48 equations). Document these equations in the table below.

Recording Observations: Record your observations in your lab journal for each reaction. Then transcribe these observations into the table below.

Reactants	Equations	Observations
$Ba(NO_3)_2 + NaCl$		
$Ba(NO_3)_2 + NaI$		
$Ba(NO_3)_2 + Na_2SO_4$		
$Ba(NO_3)_2 + Na_2CO_3$		
$AgNO_3 + NaCl$		
$AgNO_3 + NaI$		
$AgNO_3 + Na_2SO_4$		
$AgNO_3 + Na_2CO_3$		

Reactants	Equations	Observations
$Pb(NO_3)_2$ + NaCl		
$Pb(NO_3)_2$ + NaI		
$Pb(NO_3)_2$ + Na_2SO_4		
$Pb(NO_3)_2$ + Na_2CO_3		
$Cu(NO_3)_2$ + NaCl		
$Cu(NO_3)_2$ + NaI		
$Cu(NO_3)_2$ + Na_2SO_4		
$Cu(NO_3)_2$ + Na_2CO_3		

Part 2: Precipitate–nitric acid reactions

Based upon the data, create a table similar to the table above in Part 1 depicting the complete molecular equation, compete ionic equation, and net ionic equation, along with your observations if any. Remember, the precipitate and nitric acid are the reactants.

Your Name	

Part 3: Identification of unknown solutions

1. Create a precipitation matrix of your unidentified solutions, similar to the table in Part 1. Complete the table with your observations.

Your Name	

2. Create a table with your observations after the addition of nitric acid.

3. Based upon your data, determine the identity of the four unidentified solutions. Explain your conclusions by incorporating the solubility rules and results of adding nitric acid.

Your Name	

Questions

1. Which precipitates dissociated in nitric acid? Why? Why did the other precipitates remain solid?

2. Explain your train of thought for deducing the identity of the unidentified compounds.

3. Write a balanced chemical equation demonstrating how you could prepare each of the following products using two aqueous solutions or an aqueous solution with acid.

   a. $Cu_3(PO_4)_2(s)$

   b. $CO_2(g)$

   c. $CdS(s)$

   d. $NiCO_3(s)$

   e. $H_2O(l)$

Experiment 11
Acid-Base Titration

11

Text Connections
- *General Chemistry*, Sections 11.3.1–11.3.6
- *Chemistry for Accelerated Students*, Sections 9.3.1–9.3.6

Objective

First, to standardize the molarity of a sodium hydroxide solution. Second, to determine the amount of an unknown acid in solution using titration.

New Lab Skills Focus for Experiment 11

1. Standardizing a solution
2. Use of pH indicators

Apparatus

aluminum foil squares, approx. 2" × 2" (6)
balance
beaker, 600 mL
buret, 50 mL
buret clamp

Erlenmeyer flask, 250 mL (6)
filter funnel
graduated cylinder, 100 mL
ring stand
weigh boats or weighing paper

Chemicals

bromothymol blue solution
CO_2-free water (see Notes to Instructors for preparation)

NaOH solution, 0.1 M
potassium hydrogen phthalate (KHP)
unknown solid mixture of KHP and NaCl

Safety

Always follow the general safety practices described in the Preface for Students. In particular, the following safety precautions should be taken during this experiment:

1. Wear nitrile gloves whenever handling any substances.
2. Wear appropriate laboratory eye protection at all times.
3. Wear a laboratory apron to protect your clothing.

Background

A neutralization reaction occurs between an acid and a base to produce a salt and water. The H^+ ions in the aqueous acid solution react with the OH^- ions in the aqueous base solution to form water, while the remaining anions from the acid and cations from the base produce a salt solution.

An example is the neutralization of a strong acid, such as HCl, with a strong base, such as NaOH:

$$HCl(aq) + NaOH(aq) \rightarrow NaCl(aq) + H_2O(l)$$

If we write the ionic equation for this reaction and eliminate the spectator ions, it is clear that the protons from the acid combine with the hydroxide ions from the base to form water.

$$H^+(aq) + OH^-(aq) \rightarrow H_2O(l)$$

A neutralization reaction between a strong acid and a strong base is complete when equal mole amounts of both acid and base are present, which produces a salt solution with a pH of 7 (at 25°C). In this experiment you will investigate the strong acid/strong base reaction. You will investigate neutralization between a weak acid and a strong base in Experiment 16.

The common laboratory technique of *titration* allows us to conduct neutralization reactions to completion using a precise method. The process involves the slow addition of an acid (or base) to a base (or acid) in the presence of an *indicator*. Indicators are *halochromic* compounds, which means they change color based upon the pH of the solution. There are a number of indicators to choose from, but using the proper indicator for your experiment can show you when you have reached the equivalence point, the point where the acid and base exist in stoichiometrically equal amounts. This is the point of neutralization, and results in a solution pH of 7 in the case of a strong acid/strong base neutralization. Bromothymol blue will be used as the indicator in this experiment because its transition interval is 6.0–7.6. This range includes 7.0, the expected pH of the neutralized solution.

Titration is used to determine the unknown concentration of one of the reactants by adding a known amount of an acid or base with known concentration until the equivalence point is reached. A burette containing the solution with the known concentration, or *titrant*, is placed above an Erlenmeyer flask containing a small, precisely measured amount of the solution with the unknown concentration, the *analyte*. The analyte also contains a few drops of indicator. The titrant is added slowly to the analyte, and each time the flask is swirled to mix the contents. Once the indicator has changed color, the *end point* of the titration has been achieved. As described in the text, the end point is related to the equivalence point, but they are not identical, in general. The end point refers to the point where the indicator in the analyte solution changes color permanently. Depending on the indicator, the end point can be the same as or very close to the equivalence point and is used as an estimate for the equivalence point.

The concentration of the analyte can be easily calculated by determining the number of moles of titrant used to neutralize the analyte.

moles = (molarity) · (volume in L)

The mole ratio between the titrant and the analyte in the balanced chemical equation is used to determine the number of moles of analyte. Then the molarity of the analyte can be calculated by dividing the amount of analyte (moles) by the volume of analyte.

The solution with the unknown concentration can also be the titrant and the known concentration can be the analyte. So long as volumes are recorded accurately for both solutions, it does not matter.

You will investigate the neutralization reaction between potassium hydrogen phthalate (KHP) and sodium hydroxide. KHP, whose complete formula is $KHC_8H_4O_4$, is an acidic ionic compound with a very stable pH that is commonly used to *standardize* (determine the concentration of) basic solutions.

The reaction between KHP and sodium hydroxide is as follows:

$$KHC_8H_4O_4(aq) + NaOH(aq) \rightarrow H_2O(l) + KNaC_8H_4O_4(aq)$$

In water, KHP dissociates to K^+ and HP^- ions. The HP^- ion is a weak acid, and as such does not completely dissociate. However, in the presence of a strong base such as NaOH, the hydrogen in the HP⁻ does dissociate completely, and the mole ratios shown in the equation above (which are all 1:1) may be used in stoichiometric calculations.

In Part 1 of the experiment, you will determine the concentration of the strong base, NaOH. In the second part of the experiment, you will use your standardized solution of NaOH to determine the percentage of KHP in an unknown solution.

Procedure

Part 1: Standardization of NaOH Solution

1. In each of three separate weigh boats, weigh about 0.3 g of KHP. In a data table in your lab journal, record the three individual masses to the nearest 0.01 g or better under Part 1—trials 1, 2, and 3, respectively.
2. Add the KHP to three labeled 250-mL Erlenmeyer flasks. Label each flask with KHP and trial 1, 2, or 3 according to the mass.
3. Obtain the CO_2-free water from your instructor.
4. Use a graduated cylinder to measure about 50 mL of CO_2-free water and add this volume to each flask. Gently swirl the flask to dissolve the KHP.
5. Add two drops of bromothymol blue solution to each flask and swirl to mix. With the indicator added, your solution will turn bright yellow. This is the color of the indicator under acidic conditions. Seal each flask with an aluminum square to prevent the introduction of excess CO_2.
6. Place the funnel in the opening of the buret. Make sure the buret stopcock is in the closed position.
7. Obtain the NaOH solution from your instructor. Carefully and slowly pour the NaOH solution into the buret up to just above the 50-mL mark.
8. Place a 600-mL waste beaker under the buret and turn the stopcock 3 times to remove any air in the tip.
9. Record the volume on the buret to the nearest 0.1 mL. This will be the initial reading for trial 1.
10. Obtain the KHP flask for trial 1. Remove the aluminum foil and place the flask under the buret.
11. Slowly begin adding the NaOH solution to the flask, one turn at a time. After each turn, swirl the flask to mix the contents.
12. You will notice a faint blue or green color appearing every time the NaOH is added. Eventually, the green or blue-green color will remain after swirling. This is the endpoint of the titration and the trial is complete. Record the volume on the buret. This is the final volume for trial 1.
13. Repeat steps 9–12 with the remaining two KHP samples.
14. Calculate the molarity of the NaOH solution for each of the three trials. The calculations should agree within 0.5%. If not, repeat again with another trial.
15. The average of the acceptable calculations represents the molarity of the NaOH solution. This standardized NaOH solution will be used in Part 2.

Part 2: Determination of the Percentage of KHP in Solution.

1. Obtain the unknown solid mixture from your instructor.
2. Into each of three separate weigh boats, weigh about 0.3 g of the unknown. Record the three individual masses to the nearest 0.01 g or better in your data table under Part 2—trials 1, 2, and 3 respectively.

3. Add the unknown to three labeled 250-mL Erlenmeyer flasks. Label each flask with trial 1, 2, or 3 according to the mass.

4. Obtain the CO_2-free water from your instructor.

5. Use a graduated cylinder to measure about 50 mL of CO_2-free water and add this volume to each flask. Gently swirl the flask to dissolve the unknown solid mixture.

6. Add two drops of bromothymol blue solution to each flask and swirl to mix. Seal each flask with an aluminum square to prevent the introduction of excess CO_2.

7. If needed, add more NaOH solution to your buret, repeating steps 6–8 in Part 1 above.

8. Record the volume on the buret to the nearest 0.1 mL. This will be the initial reading for trial 1.

9. Obtain the flask for unknown mixture solution trial 1. Remove the aluminum foil and place the flask under the buret.

10. Slowly begin adding the NaOH solution to the flask, one turn at a time. After each turn, swirl the flask to mix the contents.

11. You will notice a faint blue or green color appearing every time the NaOH is added. Eventually, the green or blue-green color will remain after swirling. This is the endpoint of the titration and the trial is complete. Record the volume on the buret. This is the final volume for trial 1.

12. Repeat steps 8–11 with the remaining two unknown samples.

Experiment 11: Acid-Base Titration
Short Form Report Sheet

Your Name	

Your instructor will determine whether you will write a complete lab report for this experiment or use the following short form report sheet.

Part 1: Standardization of NaOH Solution

1. Create a data table below for KHP in trials 1, 2, and 3. Include the mass of KHP, moles of KHP, initial volume of NaOH, final volume of NaOH, ΔV NaOH, moles of NaOH, and molarity of NaOH.

2. Calculate the average molarity of the NaOH from the three trials.

Part 2: Determination of the Percentage of KHP in Solution.

1. Below, create another data table similar to the data table in Part 1.

Your Name	

2. For Unknown trial 1, 2, and 3, determine the mass of KHP in the unknown solid mixture.

3. Determine the percentage of KHP for each trial.

Questions

1. Calculate the sample standard deviation[1] for the molarity of NaOH calculated in Part 1. Assess the accuracy of your results.

2. Calculate the sample standard deviation for the percentage of KHP present in the unknown solid of Part 2. Assess the accuracy of your results.

---

1 For those unfamiliar with the sample standard deviation, a short tutorial is on the next page.

A Tutorial on Standard Deviation

No doubt, you are already familiar with the statistical parameters *mean* and *median*. In the language of statistics, these parameters are *measures of center*—they indicate where the "middle" of a data set is. The *standard deviation* of a data set is another statistical parameter, one that indicates the amount of "spread" in the data set. There are two different calculations for the standard deviation: the population standard deviation (σ) and the sample standard deviation (*s*). The sample standard deviation is the one most commonly used with scientific data, and is the topic in this tutorial.

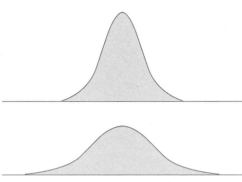

11-1. Gaussian distributions: narrow (top), and wide (bottom).

When taking measurements or performing calculations from repeated trials of an experiment, the values of the measurements—if there are enough of them—generally form a *Gaussian distribution*. Figure 11-1 shows two typical Gaussian distributions, the second distribution more spread out than the first.

The standard deviation, *s*, of a data set is a measure of how spread out the data are. Larger values of *s* mean wider spread; smaller values of *s* mean a narrower spread. The more accurate your experimental methods, and the more precise your instruments, the narrower the spread in the data should be (all else being equal). Data that are very close together will have a very small value of *s*—exactly what you want. If all the data have exactly the same value, then *s* = 0.

To help you understand the standard deviation a bit more, Figure 11-2 indicates the relationship between the standard deviation of a data set and the shape of the data distribution (assuming a Gaussian distribution). The mean of the distribution is in the center, where the zero is on the horizontal scale. The scale is marked off in increments of one standard deviation: 1*s*, 2*s*, and so on. In a Gaussian data distribution, 68% of the data values will lie within one standard deviation of the mean, 95.4% of the data will lie within two standard deviations of the mean, and 99.7% of the data will lie within three standard deviations of the mean. Note that the units for *s* are the same as the units of the data. If your data are in mL, *s* will also be in mL. If the mean of the data is 75.5 mL and *s* = 3.1 mL, then 68% of the data lie between 72.4 mL and 78.6 mL. If *s* is only 1.1 mL, then 68% of the data lie between 74.4 mL and 76.6 mL—a narrower distribution with less *uncertainty* in the measurements.

The sample standard deviation is often used as a measure of uncertainty in a data set. All measurements contain error; that's just a fact of life. All measurements made with enough precision will show a distribution in their values, and thus there is uncertainty as to the true value of the parameter being measured.

Quoting the value of *s* for a set of data is a very common way of indicating the uncertainty in the data.

Finally, the formula for calculating *s* is complicated and quite tedious to carry out. Unless you are a true statistics geek, don't bother with it here. All computer spreadsheet applications and graphing calculators will calculate the sample standard deviation. Just enter your data and look up how to run the calculation of the sample standard deviation on your device.

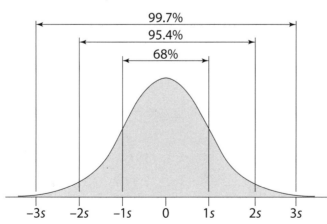

11-2. Relationship between the standard deviation and the area under the curve for a Gaussian distribution.

Experiment 12
Effectiveness of Antacids

12

Text Connections
- *General Chemistry*, Sections 11.3.4–11.3.6
- *Chemistry for Accelerated Students*, Sections 9.3.4–9.3.6

Objective

To use the technique of back titration to analyze the effectiveness of different types of antacids.

New Lab Skills Focus for Experiment 12

Back titration

Apparatus

beaker, 400 mL
buret, 50 mL
buret clamp
Erlenmeyer flask, 125 mL (3 per antacid)

filter funnel
graduated cylinder, 50 mL
ring stand
wash bottle with distilled water

Chemicals

antacid compounds
HCl, 0.1 M

litmus solution
NaOH, 0.1 M

Safety

Always follow the general safety practices described in the Preface for Students. In particular, the following safety precautions should be taken during this experiment:

1. Wear nitrile gloves whenever handling any substances.
2. Wear appropriate laboratory eye protection at all times.
3. Wear a laboratory apron to protect your clothing.

Background

Antacids are pharmaceutical compounds designed to reduce the proton content of a solution—specifically, to reduce the acid in a person's stomach. The human stomach contains hydrochloric acid and normally has a pH range of 1.0–2.0. pH levels lower than the normal range trigger the feeling of upset stomach, and therefore the motivation for antacid treatment.

Antacids can be composed of a base to perform a neutralization reaction. For example, Milk of Magnesia contains magnesium hydroxide, $Mg(OH)_2$, as the active ingredient. $Mg(OH)_2$ will neutralize the abundance of HCl in the stomach by the following neutralization reaction:

$$Mg(OH)_2(aq) + HCl(aq) \rightarrow MgCl_2(aq) + H_2O(l)$$

Other antacids buffer[1] excess acid in the stomach. A buffer is a substance that can resist changes in pH. The more common buffering antacids contain calcium carbonate, $CaCO_3$, or sodium bicarbonate, $NaHCO_3$. For example, the antacid Tums is composed of calcium carbonate, $CaCO_3$. A buffer system is established in the stomach with the following two-step process:

Step 1: $CaCO_3(aq) + HCl(aq) \rightarrow HCO_3^-(aq) + CaCl_2(aq)$

Step 2: $HCO_3^-(aq) + HCl(aq) \rightarrow H_2O(l) + CO_2(g)$

The overall reaction from a buffering antacid:

$CaCO_3(aq) + 2HCl(aq) \rightarrow CaCl_2(aq) + H_2O(l) + CO_2(g)$

Once again, the excess acid in the stomach gets neutralized into a neutral ionic salt and water, with the addition of carbon dioxide gas (technically referred to as a burp).

In this experiment you will analyze the effectiveness of different antacid compounds by using the technique of *back titration*. Experiments 8 and 11 introduced you to titration. The technique of back titration is a bit different. Back titration allows you to determine the concentration of an analyte, in this case the antacid, by reacting the antacid with an excess amount of 0.1 *M* HCl. The remaining HCl will be neutralized by titration with 0.1 *M* NaOH. This titration shows how much excess HCl is left over after its initial reaction with the antacid, and this enables the concentration of the antacid to be calculated.

Additionally, this experiment will introduce a new indicator, *litmus* solution. Litmus is an excellent indicator to use for acid-base reactions. In acidic conditions, litmus is red. In basic conditions, litmus is blue. At a neutral pH (7), litmus turns purple.

Procedure

1. Obtain the antacid samples from your instructor. You will also receive the name of the antacid, the chemical identity, and the milligram amount present in each dose. You will test each antacid according to the prescribed dose and repeat the test for a total of three trials.
2. Create a data table in your lab journal for three trials per antacid. Include the antacid name, chemical compound, milligram amount/dose, volume of HCl, initial volume of NaOH, final volume of NaOH, and ΔV of NaOH.
3. Place one antacid dose into a 125-mL Erlenmeyer flask.
4. Measure about 25 mL of 0.1 *M* HCl in a graduated cylinder and record the volume in your data table.
5. Add the HCl into the flask containing the antacid. Swirl the flask to mix the contents. The HCl should readily dissolve the antacid. Record any changes you observe, including initial color of the solution and gas production.
6. Add three drops of litmus solution to the flask and swirl. (The addition of litmus should change the color of the solution to red. If a blue or purple color appears, more HCl must be added. Add 5 mL of HCl to the solution and swirl. Continue until the red color appears. Record the final volume of HCl added.)
7. Place the funnel in the opening of the buret. Make sure the stopcock is in the closed position.
8. Obtain the 0.1 *M* NaOH solution from your instructor. Carefully, and slowly, pour the

---

1   The details of how buffering works go beyond our treatment here but are discussed in Section 11.2.3 of *Chemistry for Accelerated Students*.

NaOH solution into the buret up to just above the 50-mL mark.

9. Place the 600-mL waste beaker under the buret and turn the stopcock 3 times to remove any air in the tip.

10. Record the volume on the buret to the nearest 0.1 mL. This will be the initial reading for trial 1.

11. Place the flask containing your antacid, HCl, and litmus under the buret.

12. Slowly begin adding the NaOH solution to the flask, one turn at a time. After each turn, swirl the flask to mix the contents.

13. You will notice a faint purple color appearing every time the NaOH is added. Eventually, the faint purple color will remain after swirling. This is the endpoint of the titration and indicates a pH of 7. The trial is complete. Record the volume on the buret. This is the final volume for trial 1. If the solution has turned blue, too much NaOH was added during titration and the trial must be repeated.

14. Repeat steps 3–13 for two more trials with the same antacid.

15. Repeat steps 3–14 with the remaining antacid samples.

Experiment 12: Effectiveness of Antacids
Short Form Report Sheet

Your Name	

Your instructor will determine whether you will write a complete lab report for this experiment or use the following short form report sheet.

1. Write the balanced reactions between HCl and the antacids tested in your experiment.

2. Using the data collected for each sample, calculate the volume of HCl neutralized by NaOH.

3. Determine the volume of HCl neutralized by the antacid for each trial.

4. Using your HCl solution volume data and the mass and chemical identity of each antacid, determine the molarity of each antacid.

Questions

1. Could this experiment been performed by dissolving the antacid in water, then titrating with 0.1 M HCl? Explain.

2. List the effectiveness of each antacid from greatest (neutralized the greatest volume of HCl) to weakest (neutralized the least volume of HCl).

3. Is there a relationship between antacid strength and the molarity of the antacid? Explain.

Experiment 13
Calorimetry and Hess's Law

13

Text Connections
- *General Chemistry*, N/A
- *Chemistry for Accelerated Students*, Sections 6.2.7, 10.2.1, 10.2.2

Objectives

1. To demonstrate proficiency in using a calorimeter.
2. To relate temperature change to enthalpy of reaction for a series of related reactions.
3. To verify Hess's law by confirming the additive enthalpy changes of reactions to the enthalpy change of the overall reaction.

New Lab Skills Focus for Experiment 13

Construction and use of a simple calorimeter

Apparatus

balance
graduated cylinder, 100-mL (2)
graduated cylinder, 250-mL
polystyrene (Styrofoam) cup with lid
scoopula

stirrer for calorimeter (See Notes to Instructors for calorimeter details)
thermometer
weigh boat or weighing paper

Chemicals

distilled water
HCl solution, 0.5 *M*
HCl solution, 1.0 *M*

NaOH pellets
NaOH solution, 1.0 *M*

Safety

Always follow the general safety practices described in the Preface for Students. In particular, the following safety precautions should be taken during this experiment:

1. Wear nitrile gloves whenever handling any substances.
2. Wear appropriate laboratory eye protection at all times.
3. Wear a laboratory apron to protect your clothing.

Background

In 1840, Germain Hess (Russia, 1802–1850) published his law of constant heat summation, now known as Hess's law.[1] Hess's law states that the enthalpy change for a reaction is the same regardless of whether the reaction occurs in multiple steps or in one step. This law has enabled scientists to use a series of reactions to determine the enthalpy change for a single reaction even when that enthalpy change cannot be measured directly.

---

1   American orthography would normally have us write Hess' law. However, the British orthography with the final *s* added is used universally when referring to Hess's law.

For reactions occurring at a constant pressure, the *enthalpy change*, ΔH, is the amount of heat that flows into or out of the chemical system during the reaction. ΔH values are typically expressed in kilojoules (kJ). The enthalpy of formation, $\Delta H°_f$, is defined as the amount of heat released or absorbed when one mole of a substance is formed from its elements; $\Delta H°_f$ values are typically expressed in kJ/mol. A negative ΔH value means a reaction is exothermic, releasing energy (heat) to the surroundings. A positive ΔH value denotes an endothermic reaction, in which heat is absorbed from the surroundings.

A *calorimeter* is a device that is used to measure the temperature change of a substance undergoing a reaction, while thermally isolating the reaction from the surrounding environment. The temperature change and masses can be used to determine the enthalpy change for a reaction. The amount of energy, or heat, absorbed or released during a reaction in a calorimeter is calculated as

$$Q = Cn\Delta T$$

where Q represents the energy in J, C is the molar heat capacity in J/(mol·K), n is the number of moles, and ΔT is the change in temperature in °C (defined as $T_f - T_i$). For reactions in aqueous solution, a reaction that releases heat—meaning a negative value for ΔH—will warm up the water, resulting in a positive value for ΔT and a positive value for Q. So make note of this important detail: the calorimetry value obtained for Q represents the amount of heat gained or lost to the system by the reaction that is taking place within the system, and the ΔH of the reaction will equal $-Q$.

In this experiment you will use a polystyrene (Styrofoam) cup calorimeter to perform three separate reactions:

Reaction 1: $NaOH(s) \rightarrow NaOH(aq)$

Reaction 2: $NaOH(s) + HCl(aq) \rightarrow NaCl(aq) + H_2O(l)$

Reaction 3: $NaOH(aq) + HCl(aq) \rightarrow NaCl(aq) + H_2O(l)$

When Reaction 1 is reversed and added to Reaction 2, the NaOH(s) terms cancel and Reaction 3 results:

$NaOH(aq) \rightarrow NaOH(s)$	$-\Delta H_1$
$NaOH(s) + HCl(aq) \rightarrow NaCl(aq) + H_2O(l)$	ΔH_2
$NaOH(aq) + HCl(aq) \rightarrow NaCl(aq) + H_2O(l)$	ΔH_3

Reversing Reaction 1 also reverses the sign on ΔH_1. Hess's law implies that ΔH_3 for Reaction 3 is equal to the sum of the ΔH values for Reaction 1 (reversed) and Reaction 2. One of the goals for this experiment is to verify Hess's law using ΔH_3. Note that since each equation includes one mole of NaOH, the ΔH values for each reaction (in kJ/mol) represent the amount heat absorbed per mole of NaOH.

Procedure

Prelab: Constructing the Calorimeter

1. Obtain two polystyrene cups, an insulated lid with two small holes, a thermometer, and a stirrer.[2]
2. Assemble the calorimeter apparatus as shown in Figure 13-1. (Obviously, the opening shown in the side of the calorimeter is just for the illustration. Your calorimeter will not perform well with a big hole in the side.)
3. During the reactions, hold or support the calorimeter near the top rather than at the bottom. This will keep the heat from your hand away from the reaction liquids.

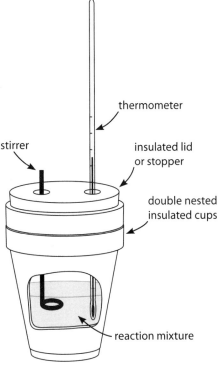

Figure 13-1. Assembled calorimeter.

Reaction 1: $NaOH(s) \rightarrow NaOH(aq)$

1. Measure about 100 mL of distilled water into a graduated cylinder. Record the volume of the water to the nearest 0.1 mL in a data table in your lab journal.
2. Pour the water into the calorimeter. Place the thermometer in the water. Once the temperature is stable, record the water temperature to the nearest 0.1°C in your data table. Note that thermometers break easily, so handle the thermometer with care and do not use it to stir the solution.
3. Using the metal scoopula, weigh about 2 g of NaOH pellets onto a weigh boat or weighing paper. Make sure the balance has been *tared* (or zeroed) for the mass of the weigh boat or weighing paper. Record the mass of the NaOH to the nearest 0.01 g or better. It is important that this step be done quickly because NaOH is *hygroscopic*, which means it absorbs moisture from the air. Thus, the mass of the NaOH will increase due to absorbed moisture as long as it remains exposed to the air.
4. Immediately place the NaOH pellets in the calorimeter cup, cover the calorimeter with the lid and gently stir the solution with the stirring rod. Watch the thermometer and record the maximum temperature to the nearest 0.1°C.
5. The reaction is finished when the temperature no longer rises, which could take up to 10 minutes or so. Dispose of the solution in your calorimeter in the container designated by the instructor for disposal of basic solutions.
6. Rinse the calorimeter, thermometer, and stirring rod and repeat Reaction 1 for a second trial.
7. Rinse the calorimeter, thermometer, and stirring rod before proceeding to the next reaction.

Reaction 2: $NaOH(s) + HCl(aq) \rightarrow NaCl(aq) + H_2O(l)$

1. Measure about 100 mL of 0.5 *M* HCl into a graduated cylinder. Record the volume to the nearest 0.1 mL.

---

2   See Notes to Instructors for details on calorimeter parts.

2. Pour the HCl solution into your calorimeter. Place the thermometer in the water. Once the temperature is stable, record the HCl temperature to the nearest 0.1°C.
3. Using the metal scoopula, weigh about 2 g of NaOH pellets onto a weigh boat or weighing paper. Make sure the balance has been tared for the mass of the weigh boat or weighing paper. Record the mass of the NaOH to the nearest 0.01 g or better. As before, it is important that this step be done quickly because NaOH is hygroscopic.
4. Immediately place the NaOH pellets in the calorimeter cup, cover the calorimeter with the lid and gently stir the solution with the stirring rod. Watch the thermometer and record the maximum temperature in your data table.
5. The reaction is finished when the temperature no longer rises. Dispose of the solution in your calorimeter in the container designated by the teacher for disposal of neutral solutions.
6. Rinse the calorimeter, thermometer, and stirring rod and repeat Reaction 2 for a second trial.

Reaction 3: $NaOH(aq) + HCl(aq) \rightarrow NaCl(aq) + H_2O(l)$

1. Measure about 50 mL of 1.0 M HCl into a graduated cylinder. Record the volume of the HCl to the nearest 0.1 mL.
2. Pour the HCl solution into your calorimeter. Record the temperature of the HCl solution to the nearest 0.1°C.
3. Measure about 50 ml of 1.0 M NaOH into a graduated cylinder. Record the volume of the NaOH solution to the nearest 0.1 mL.
4. Pour the NaOH solution into the calorimeter cup, cover the calorimeter with the lid and gently stir the solution with the stirring rod. Watch the thermometer and record the maximum temperature.
5. When finished with this reaction, pour the solution into the container designated by your teacher for disposal of neutral solutions.
6. Rinse the calorimeter, thermometer, and stirring rod and repeat Reaction 3 for a second trial.

Experiment 13: Calorimetry and Hess's Law
Short Form Report Sheet

Your Name	

Your instructor will determine whether you will write a complete lab report for this experiment or use the following short form report sheet.

Create a data table for each reaction (two trials each) showing all the data recorded in the experiment.

Questions

1. Calculate the average change in temperature, ΔT, for each of the reactions.

2. Assuming that the density of the water and the solutions is 0.998 g/mL, calculate the mass of water and the number of moles of water present for each of the reactions.

3. Using the equation $Q = Cn\Delta T$, calculate the heat released by each reaction. Use the molar heat capacity of water and the number of moles of water for all your calculations. (The water contains over 99% of the moles in each of the reactions. Using the C and n for water alone simplifies the calculations and results in an error of less than 0.2%.)

4. Calculate the number of moles of NaOH used in each of the reactions.

5. Calculate the ΔH value in kJ/mol of NaOH for each of the three reactions.

Your Name	

6. Using the values you obtained for ΔH for Reactions 1 and 2 and your knowledge of Hess's law, calculate the change in enthalpy for Reaction 3.

7. Compare your calculated ΔH value for Reaction 3 to the actual ΔH value obtained from the calorimeter by calculating the percent difference.

Experiment 14
Rate Law Determination for the Acid-Catalyzed Iodination of Acetone

14

| **Text Connections** |
| • *General Chemistry*, N/A |
| • *Chemistry for Accelerated Students*, Sections 10.4.5, 10.4.6 |

Objectives

1. To measure and compare reaction rates.
2. To determine the rate law and the rate law constant of the reaction.

New Lab Skills Focus for Experiment 14

1. Measuring reaction rate
2. Determining a rate law

Apparatus

12-well plate   toothpicks
stopwatch

Chemicals

The following solutions in dropper bottles: HCl, 1.0 *M*
   acetone, 4.0 *M*   starch solution, 1%
   distilled water
   iodine, 0.005 *M*

Safety

Always follow the general safety practices described in the Preface for Students. In particular, the following safety precautions should be taken during this experiment:

1. Wear nitrile gloves whenever handling any substances.
2. Wear appropriate laboratory eye protection at all times.
3. Wear a laboratory apron to protect your clothing.

Background

The branch of chemistry involved with studying chemical reaction rates is called *chemical kinetics*. For homogenous reactions (reactions with substances in the same state), reaction rates depend on four factors: the temperature, the properties of the reactants, the presence of a catalyst, and the concentration of the reactants. Influencing any one of these factors can ultimately speed up or slow down the reaction rate. For the typical reaction

$$A + B \rightarrow C + D$$

the reaction rate can be expressed by:

$$\text{Rate} = k[A]^x[B]^y$$

The rate of the reaction, measured in *M*/sec, is dependent upon the molar concentration of the reactants A and B. The *rate constant, k,* is specific to a particular reaction at particular temperature. The exponents *x* and *y* are called the *orders* of reaction with respect to substances A and B. The orders of reaction are typically integers from 0 to 3. These values are determined experimentally and the sum of the orders for the individual reactants provides the overall order for the reaction.

This experiment will allow you to calculate the orders of reaction for each reactant for the reaction between iodine and acetone. By performing multiple reactions with varying concentrations of the reactants, you will be able to determine how the rate is affected by the reactant concentration. Additionally, you will be able to calculate the rate constant, *k*, for this reaction.

The reaction between acetone (C_3H_6O or CH_3CH_3CO) and iodine occurs in the presence of an acid catalyst, in this case HCl. The reaction may be represented using structural formulas as follows:

Accordingly, the reaction rate depends on the molar concentration of the catalyst as well as the molar concentrations of the two reactants. The rate law can be written as:

$$\text{Rate} = k\left[C_3H_6O\right]^x\left[I_2\right]^y\left[HCl\right]^z \qquad (1)$$

The *iodination* of acetone is a convenient reaction for studying rate laws because the experimenter can visually determine when the reaction is complete. In the presence of starch, iodine (I_2) exhibits a characteristic blue-black color. The disappearance of the blue-black color signifies that all the iodine has reacted and the reaction is complete. The rate of the reaction can be calculated by the change in iodine concentration divided by the change in time:

$$\text{Rate} = \frac{-\Delta\left[I_2\right]}{\Delta t} = \frac{-\left(\left[I_2\right]_{final} - \left[I_2\right]_{initial}\right)}{\Delta t} = \frac{\left[I_2\right]_{initial}}{\Delta t} \qquad (2)$$

(See footnote.[1])

The negative sign is present to allow the rate to be positive since we can assume the final iodine concentration is equal to zero. The orders of the individual reactants can be determined by comparing the reaction rates to the differing concentrations of reactants. Once all the orders are known, you can use them and one of the rates to calculate the rate constant.

You will conduct the iodination reaction with four separate sets of concentrations. We will calls these Reaction 1, 2, 3, and 4. For each set of concentrations you will conduct three trials of the reaction. For each reaction, the starch, iodine and HCl solutions are combined first. The reaction begins when the acetone solution is added.

---

[1]   Equation (2) is an approximation—a remarkably simple one—and implies that the reaction rate is constant, regardless of $[I_2]$. The reaction rate can only be constant because of the special circumstances of this reaction, namely, the order of $[I_2]$ in the rate law, Equation (1), and the relative values of $[C_3H_6O]$ and $[HCl]$, both of which are much greater than $[I_2]$. When you determine the order of $[I_2]$ in the rate law, you will hopefully see why Equation (2) is a valid approximation for this reaction.

Reaction Matrix				
Reaction Number	1% starch (drops)	0.0050 M I_2 (drops)	1.0 M HCl (drops)	4.0 M acetone (drops)
1	10 + 10 drops of water	10	10	10
2	10	10	10	20
3	10	10	20	10
4	10	20	10	10

Table 14-1. Reaction matrix for iodination of acetone.

The reaction rates for the three trials of a reaction should be consistent. (If they are not, review your procedure for adding acetone and operating the stopwatch.) You will use the average of the three trials as the rate for a given reaction.

Note that the starch is only present to act as a color indicator for the concentration of iodine. The starch plays no role in the iodination reaction itself.

Procedure

1. Obtain a 12-well plate. Label the columns with the reactions numbers 1, 2, 3, and 4. The three wells in each column are for the three trials of a particular reaction.
2. Obtain dropper bottles of distilled water and solutions of starch, iodine, HCl, and acetone.
3. Using the reaction matrix shown in Table 14-1, add the designated number of drops of water, starch, iodine, and HCl into the three wells for Reaction 1. *Reserve the acetone until the next step.*
4. Before the acetone is added to the first Reaction 1 well, one team member should be ready to start the stopwatch, while the other team member adds the acetone.
5. Quickly add the designated number of drops of acetone to the first Reaction 1 well. Start the stopwatch when the first drop is added. Continually stir the solution in the well with a toothpick until the blue-black color disappears.
6. Once the color has disappeared, stop the stopwatch and record the time in a data table in your lab journal.
7. Repeat this procedure for the remaining Reaction 1 wells, which are trials 2 and 3 of the same reaction.
8. Repeat steps 3–7 for Reactions 2–4.

Experiment 14: Rate Law Determination for the Acid-Catalyzed Iodination of Acetone
Short Form Report Sheet

Your Name	

Your instructor will determine whether you will write a complete lab report for this experiment or use the following short form report sheet.

Create a data table for the four reactions and the three trials of each. Include space for the concentrations of the reactants in the mixture, the rate in M/sec for each reaction, and the calculation for the rate constant, k.

Using the relation $M_1V_1 = M_2V_2$, you can calculate the molarity of each the three reactants in the reaction solution. M_1 and V_1 represent the reactant molarity and number of drops of reactant added to the reaction solution. In each reaction, V_2 is equal to 50, the total number of drops in the reaction solution. M_2 is then the molarity of the reactant in the reaction solution.

Questions

1. Comparing any two reactions, if the concentration of a reactant doubles (other concentrations held constant) and the rate doubles, the reaction rate is first order for that reactant. If the concentration doubles and the rate quadruples, the reaction is second order for that reactant. If the concentration changes but the rate does not, the reaction order is zero and the reactant in question does not appear in the rate law.[1] Determine the reaction orders for acetone, iodine, and HCl in the iodination of acetone. What is the overall order for this reaction?

2. Use the concentrations, orders, and reaction rate for one of the reactions to determine the rate constant and write the rate law for the iodination of acetone.

3. Calculate the reaction rate if the concentrations are $[C_3H_6O] = 0.50\ M$, $[I_2] = 0.50\ M$, and $[HCl] = 0.50\ M$.

---

1   See Section 10.4.5 and Example 10.6 in *Chemistry for Accelerated Students* for more detail.

Experiment 15
Le Châtelier's Principle

15

Text Connections
- *General Chemistry*, N/A
- *Chemistry for Accelerated Students*, Sections 11.1.4, 11.1.5

Objectives

To predict and observe the shift in equilibrium reactions due to specific system stresses.

New Lab Skills Focus for Experiment 15

Use of ice water and boiling water baths

Apparatus

24-well plate

boiling water bath

ice water bath

test tubes, small (8)

test tube holder

test tube rack

toothpicks

Chemicals

The following solutions in dropper bottles:

$AgNO_3$, 0.1 M

$CoCl_2$, 1.0 M

distilled water

$Fe(NO_3)_3$, 0.01 M

HCl, 12.0 M

HNO_3, 6.0 M

K_2CrO_4, 0.1 M

Na_2HPO_4, 0.1 M

NaOH, 0.1 M

NaSCN, 0.01 M

NH_3, 15.0 M

$NiCl_2$ 0.1 M

Safety

Always follow the general safety practices described in the Preface for Students. In particular, the following safety precautions should be taken during this experiment:

1. Wear nitrile gloves whenever handling any substances.
2. Wear appropriate laboratory eye protection at all times.
3. Wear a laboratory apron to protect your clothing.

Background

The majority of the reactions you have studied so far have gone to completion. In other words, the reaction proceeded in one direction and the reactants reacted to form products. However, many reactions do not proceed this way; a reverse reaction from products to reactants is also present. These types of reactions will reach a state of chemical equilibrium when the rate of the forward reaction (reactants → products) equals the rate of the reverse reaction (reactants ← products).

La Châtelier's Principle, first proposed by Henry Louis Le Châtelier, states that a reaction in chemical equilibrium will remain at equilibrium unless the equilibrium experiences a change in concentration, volume, pressure, or temperature. If a change, or stress, does occur, the equilibrium will shift to overcome the stress and a new equilibrium will be established.

In this experiment, you will study classic equilibrium reactions and specific stresses to the equilibrium to trigger a shift to favor the reactants or the products in the equilibrium reaction. This will be accomplished by changing the concentrations of the substances in the reaction by adding or removing substances, and by changing the temperature.

Consider the equilibrium expression:

$$A + B \rightleftharpoons C + D + \text{heat}$$

Le Châtelier's Principle allows us to predict the equilibrium shift based upon the type of stress the equilibrium undergoes. The shift will either favor the production of reactants (shift to the left) or products (shift to the right). If more A is added to the reaction, the equilibrium will shift to the right and the concentration of products will rise. Similarly, if more C is added to the reaction, the equilibrium will shift to the left, favoring production of the reactants. However, if a quantity of A or B is removed from the system, the equilibrium will shift to the left to compensate for its loss.

In the forward direction, the above reaction is exothermic due to the production of heat. This means if the reaction vessel is heated, the equilibrium will shift to the left. Conversely, if the reaction is cooled, the equilibrium will shift to the right, favoring heat production.

In this experiment you will study four equilibrium reactions:

Reaction 1: $Co(H_2O)_6^{2+}(aq) + 4Cl^-(aq) \rightleftharpoons CoCl_4^{2-}(aq) + 6H_2O(l)$

Technically, this is the net ionic equation for the reaction between $CoCl_2$ and HCl. The cobalt ion Co^{2+} forms a *complex ion* with six water molecules and has a characteristic pink color. When Co^{2+} reacts with high concentrations of Cl^- ions, a new complex ion between Co^{2+} and Cl^- is produced, which has a characteristic blue color. A complex ion is a covalent compound with a metallic central atom and a *dative* sharing of electrons. Instead of each atom contributing one electron to the covalent bond, one atom donates two electrons to complete the bond. This is called a *coordinate* or *dative* covalent bond. Since an atom is donating an electron pair, the atom may be described as acting like a Lewis base. Water, ammonia (NH_3), and chloride (Cl^-) are common in the formation of such complex ions.

Reaction 2: $Fe^{3+}(aq) + SCN^-(aq) \rightleftharpoons FeSCN^{2+}(aq)$

This is the net ionic equation for the reaction between $Fe(NO_3)_3$ and sodium thiocyanate (NaSCN). Once again we see a complex ion, $FeSCN^{2+}$, produced from the reaction of Fe^{3+} and SCN^-. In solution, the Fe^{3+} ion has a characteristic pale yellow color, while the $FeSCN^{2+}$ ion is red.

Reaction 3: $2CrO_4^{2-}(aq) + 2H^+(aq) \rightleftharpoons Cr_2O_7^{2-}(aq) + H_2O(l)$

This is the net ionic equation for the reaction between K_2CrO_4 and HNO_3. The chromate ion, CrO_4^{2-}, is yellow, while the dichromate ion, $Cr_2O_7^{2-}$, is red.

Reaction 4: $Ni(H_2O)_6^{2+}(aq) + 6NH_3(aq) \rightleftharpoons Ni(NH_3)_6^{2+}(aq) + 6H_2O(l)$

This is the net ionic equation for the reaction between $NiCl_2$ and NH_3. Again, a complex ion forms between Ni^{2+} and water. When Ni^{2+} reacts with high concentrations of NH_3, a new com-

Reaction Matrix						
	1	2	3	4	5	6
A Reaction 1	10 drops CoCl$_2$	7 drops CoCl$_2$ + 3 drops HCl or until color changes	Same drops as A2, + 5 drops H$_2$O	Same drops as A2, + 5 additional drops of HCl	Same drops as A2, + 5 drops of AgNO$_3$	blank
B Reaction 2	10 drops Fe(NO$_3$)$_3$	5 drops Fe(NO$_3$)$_3$ + 5 drops NaSCN	Same drops as B2, + 5 additional drops Fe(NO$_3$)$_3$	Same drops as B2, + 5 drops NaSCN	Same drops as B2, + 5 drops Na$_2$HPO$_4$	blank
C Reaction 3	10 drops K$_2$CrO$_4$	5 drops K$_2$CrO$_4$ + 5 drops HNO$_3$ or until color changes	Same drops as C2, + 5 drops H$_2$O	Same drops as C2, + 5 drops HCl	Same drops as C2, + 5 drops NaOH	Same drops as C2, + 5 drops AgNO$_3$
D Reaction 4	10 drops NiCl$_2$	10 drops NiCl$_2$ + 3 drops NH$_3$ or until color changes	Same drops as D2, + 5 drops H$_2$O	Same drops as D2, + 5 drops HCl	Same drops as D2, + 5 drops NaOH	blank

Table 15-1. Reaction matrix for the four reactions.

plex ion between Ni^{2+} and NH_3 is produced, $Ni(NH_3)_6^{2+}$. $Ni(H_2O)_6^{2+}$ has a characteristic green color, while the $Ni(NH_3)_6^{2+}$ ion is pale violet in color.

Procedure

1. Obtain a 24-well plate. Label the four rows with the reactions numbers 1, 2, 3, and 4.
2. Obtain dropper bottles of all chemicals listed in the chemicals list.
3. Using the reaction matrix shown in Table 15-1, add the designated number of drops of each substance. If necessary, use a toothpick to mix the contents in the well. (Use a different toothpick for each well.) The first well in a row serves as a color reference for the reactant color. The second well is the reference for the color that reaction achieves at equilibrium. The remaining wells in the row represent different stresses to affect the equilibrium.
4. Record the color of each well after all solutions have been added. If no color change occurs in a given well, continue adding the last substance drop-wise in the well until a change does occur.
5. Obtain two test tubes for each reaction. For each reaction, label one tube 1C and the other 1H (for Reaction 1 cold water and Reaction 1 hot water, respectively).
6. Place each tube securely in the test tube rack.
7. Drop the following amounts of each substance into each tube:

Reaction 1	Reaction 2	Reaction 3	Reaction 4
20 drops CoCl$_2$ + HCl until color changes	15 drops Fe(NO$_3$)$_3$ + 15 drops NaSCN	15 drops K$_2$CrO$_4$ + 15 drops HNO$_3$	20 drops NiCl$_2$ + NH$_3$ until color changes

8. Using the test tube holder, carefully hold each "C" tube in the ice water bath. Record any color change and place the test tube back in the test tube rack.
9. Using the test tube holder, carefully hold each "H" tube in the boiling water bath. Record any color change and place the test tube back in the test tube rack.

Experiment 15: Le Châtelier's Principle
Short Form Report Sheet

Your Name	

Your instructor will determine whether you will write a complete lab report for this experiment or use the following short form report sheet.

Create a data table for the four reactions performed in the 24-well plate and test tubes. Include the contents in each well and tube and the color change noted in each case.

Questions

Explain your observations for each reaction, addressing the following questions: Why did the addition of a specific substance trigger a color change? Which direction did the equilibrium shift? Did the addition of one of the substances produce a precipitate? If so, identify the precipitate and the effect it had on equilibrium. Was the reaction endothermic or exothermic? How do you know?

Reaction 1: $Co(H_2O)_6^{2+}(aq) + 4Cl^-(aq) \rightleftharpoons CoCl_4^{2-}(aq) + 6H_2O(l)$

Reaction 2: $Fe^{3+}(aq) + SCN^-(aq) \rightleftharpoons FeSCN^{2+}(aq)$

Reaction 3: $2CrO_4^{2-}(aq) + 2H^+(aq) \rightleftharpoons Cr_2O_7^{2-}(aq) + H_2O(l)$

Reaction 4: $Ni(H_2O)_6^{2+}(aq) + 6NH_3(aq) \rightleftharpoons Ni(NH_3)_6^{2+}(aq) + 6H_2O(l)$

Experiment 16
Titration Curves and K_a

16

Text Connections
- *General Chemistry*, Sections 11.3.4, 11.3.5
- *Chemistry for Accelerated Students*, Sections 9.3.4, 9.3.5

Objectives

To compare titration curves to predicted K_a values.

New Lab Skills Focus for Experiment 16

Analysis of titration curves

Apparatus

beaker, 600-mL
beaker, 250-mL (6)
buret, 50-mL
buret clamp
filter funnel

graduated cylinder, 50-mL
magnetic stir plate (if available)
pH meter, digital
ring stand

Chemicals

acetic acid, 0.1 *M*
NaOH, 0.1 *M*
oxalic acid, 0.1 *M*

Safety

Always follow the general safety practices described in the Preface for Students. In particular, the following safety precautions should be taken during this experiment:

1. Wear nitrile gloves whenever handling any substances.
2. Wear appropriate laboratory eye protection at all times.
3. Wear a laboratory apron to protect your clothing.

Background

Our previous experiments have introduced two acid-base indicator solutions, bromothymol blue and litmus. Both of these indicators are good to use for strong acid-strong base neutralization reactions due to the fact that the color change (end point) for both indicators occurs at a pH of 7. In the case of a strong acid-strong base titration, the end point is very close to the equivalence point of the titration. Recall that the equivalence point is the point during titration when the mole amount of the titrant is equal to the mole amount of the analyte.

When a titration is performed with a weak acid and a strong base or a strong acid and a weak base, the equivalence point does not always occur at a pH of 7. This is due to the fact that the anions of weak acids are strong enough bases to accept some protons from water molecules, creating OH^- ions and increasing the pH, an effect known as *anion hydrolysis*. Likewise, the cations of weak bases are strong enough acids to donate protons (if they have any hydrogen atoms, such as in the case of bases containing NH_4^+) to water molecules to form H_3O^+ ions, thus lowering the

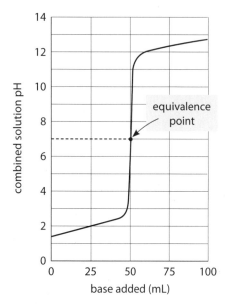

Figure 16-1. Change in the pH of the combined solution as a strong acid is titrated with a strong base.

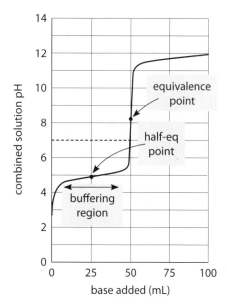

Figure 16-2. Change in the pH of the combined solution as a weak acid is titrated with a strong base.

pH (*cation hydrolysis*).[1] Put another way, a weak acid or a weak base does not completely dissociate in solution, and the conjugate base or acid formed by the partial dissociation is strong enough to affect the pH. This effect can be best visualized by analyzing a titration curve.

A titration curve shows the pH of a solution versus the volume of base added during the titration. A typical titration curve between a strong acid and a strong base is shown in Figure 16-1.

Lots of information can be obtained from a titration curve. As base is added to the acid, the pH levels rise only slightly due to the excess of H^+ ions in solution. However, once all the H^+ ions have been neutralized by the OH^- ions, the equivalence point is reached, and the pH rises drastically. After that point, the pH slowly rises toward the pH of the base in the titrant.

All titration curves follow the same overall shape. However, there are some key differences when a weak acid is titrated with a strong base, or conversely, a strong acid with a weak base. A typical titration curve for a weak acid (HA) and a strong base (NaOH) is shown in Figure 16-2. A reaction between a weak acid and a strong base does not have an equivalence point equal to a pH of 7. The equivalence point lies on the basic side, as explained above.

Let's now turn our attention to the region on the curve preceding the equivalence point, the area known as the *buffering region*. In this region, some of the weak acid is being converted to its conjugate base. The acid-conjugate base pair behaves like a buffer, resisting changes to pH even in the presence of a strong base like NaOH. Between the equivalence point (the steepest part of the curve) and the beginning of titration lies the *half-equivalence point*. At the half-equivalence point, enough base has been added to cause half of the weak acid to be dissociated, which means the concentration of the non-dissociated weak acid is equal to the concentration of the conjugate base of that weak acid. This occurs because the increasing quantities of OH^- ions from the base are pulling protons away from the weak acid, forcing it to dissociate and form the conjugate base.

The acid-dissociation equilibrium constant, K_a, for the weak acid is:

$$K_a = \frac{\left[H_3O^+\right]\left[A^-\right]}{\left[HA\right]}$$

---

1   For an in-depth explanation, see Section 11.2.4 in *Chemistry for Accelerated Students*.

At the half-equivalence point, $[HA] = [A^-]$, so we can rewrite the expression for K_a at the half-equivalence point as

$$K_a = \left[H_3O^+ \right]$$

Analysis of the titration curve allows us to determine the pH at the half-equivalence point. We know that

$$pH = -\log\left[H_3O^+ \right]$$

and therefore

$$\left[H_3O^+ \right] = 10^{-pH} = \text{antilog}\left(-pH \right)$$

This information allows us to calculate the K_a of the weak acid.

The goal of this experiment is to construct your own titration curves and use the data to determine the K_a of a monoprotic weak acid and a diprotic weak acid. As the name suggests, a monoprotic acid has one available proton to donate, and a diprotic acid has two. The titration curve in Figure 16-2 is typical of curves for monoprotic weak acids. A titration curve for a diprotic weak acid essentially represents two titrations, one for each proton, as shown in Figure 16-3.

The titration curve clearly shows two equivalence points, each preceded by a half-equivalence point. From these data, one can calculate a K_{a1} and K_{a2} for the respective half-equivalence points.

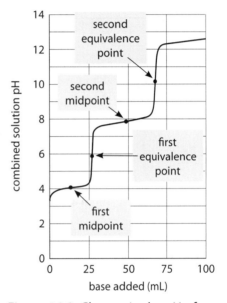

Figure 16-3. Change in the pH of the combined solution as a diprotic weak acid is titrated with a strong base.

Procedure

Part 1: Monoprotic weak acid titration curve

1. Using a graduated cylinder, measure about 25 mL of 0.1 M acetic acid (CH_3COOH) into three separate 250-mL beakers.
2. Place the funnel in the opening of the buret. Make sure the stopcock is in the closed position.
3. Obtain the 0.1 M NaOH solution from your instructor. Carefully, and slowly, pour the NaOH solution into the buret slightly past the 50-mL mark.
4. Place the 600-mL waste beaker under the buret and turn the stopcock until the meniscus reads 50 mL.
5. Record the volume on the buret to the nearest 0.1 mL. This will be the initial reading for trial 1.
6. Place a magnetic stir plate under the buret, making sure to leave room for your beaker.[2]
7. Place a magnetic stir bar in your first beaker containing the acetic acid and place the beaker

---

2   If magnetic stirrers are not available, students may manually swirl the beaker. See Notes to Instructors.

on the magnetic stir plate. Turn the stir plate on (low to medium speed).

8. Place the pH meter in the beaker, making sure to rest it near an area where it will be free from the magnetic stir bar. If needed, support the pH meter with a clamp on the ring stand.
9. Record the initial pH of the acid.
10. Add the titrant in 1-mL increments and record each volume increment to the nearest 0.1 mL. Record the pH after each increment.
11. For trials 2 and 3, repeat steps 2–10 for the remaining two samples.

Part 2: Diprotic acid titration curve

1. Using a graduated cylinder, measure about 25 mL of 0.1 M oxalic acid, $H_2C_2O_4$, into three separate 250-mL beakers.
2. Follow steps 2–10 described above in Part 1.
3. Continue adding base until you have seen the pH rise dramatically through the first and second equivalence points and the pH rises only slightly with each additional 1 mL of base.
4. For trials 2 and 3, repeat steps 1–3 for the remaining two samples.

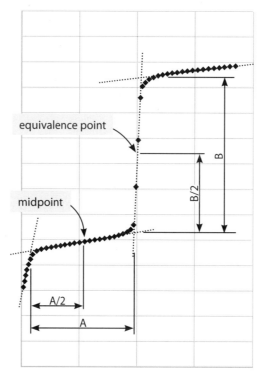

Figure 16-4. To locate the equivalence point and midpoint, draw straight lines through the straight sections of your data (shown as dotted lines in the figure). The equivalence point and midpoint are located halfway between the corners where these lines intersect.

Experiment 16: Titration Curves and K_a
Short Form Report Sheet

Your Name	

Your instructor will determine whether you will write a complete lab report for this experiment or use the following short form report sheet.

1. On a separate sheet of paper, create a data table depicting the NaOH volume (mL) and pH for the three titration trials for Parts 1 and 2.
2. On your computer, plot the titration data for each trial depicting the pH vs. volume of NaOH for Parts 1 and Part 2 (six curves total).
3. Referring to Figure 16-4 as a guide, locate and label the equivalence point(s) and half-equivalence point(s) on each curve. This is essentially a geometric exercise.
4. From your graphs, determine the pH of each solution at the half-equivalence point.
5. Determine the K_a for each acid.

Questions

1. What kind of titration curve would you expect to see with a strong acid and a weak base? Would the equivalence point be above or below pH = 7? Why?

2. The Henderson-Hasselbalch equation allows you to determine the pH of an acid at any given point along a titration curve:

$$pH = pK_a + \log\left(\frac{[A^-]}{[HA]}\right)$$

where pK_a is defined as

$$pK_a = -\log(K_a)$$

If [A-]=[HA] at the half-equivalence point, what other important piece of information can you gather about the weak acids you tested in this experiment?

3. The "overall pH" for a diprotic acid is represented by the following equation:

$$pH = \frac{pK_{a1} + pK_{a2}}{2}$$

Determine the overall pH of the oxalic acid you tested in Part 2.

Experiment 17
Determination of the Percentage of Iron in Iron Supplements—Redox Titration

17

Text Connections
- *General Chemistry*, Sections 11.3.4, 11.3.5, 12.2.1, 12.2.2
- *Chemistry for Accelerated Students*, Sections 9.3.4, 9.3.5, 12.2.1, 12.2.2

Objectives

To use redox titration methods to determine the percentage of iron in over-the-counter iron supplements.

Apparatus

balance	graduated cylinder, 10-mL
beaker, 600-mL	graduated cylinder, 100-mL
buret, 50-mL	ring stand
buret clamp	weigh boats or weighing paper
Erlenmeyer flask, 250-mL (3)	

Chemicals

H_3PO_4, 2.0 M	iron supplements
H_2SO_4, 1.0 M	$KMnO_4$, 0.02 M

Safety

Always follow the general safety practices described in the Preface for Students. In particular, the following safety precautions should be taken during this experiment:

1. Wear nitrile gloves whenever handling any substances.
2. Wear appropriate laboratory eye protection at all times.
3. Wear a laboratory apron to protect your clothing.

Background

In this experiment you will revisit the reaction between the Fe^{2+} ion and the permanganate (MnO_4^-) ion observed in the molarity experiment (Experiment 8). However, this time we will appreciate the fact that this reaction is a classic *redox reaction*. The procedure will make use of your titration skills to determine the amount of iron in over-the-counter iron supplements.

The most common form of iron in iron supplements is provided in the form of iron (II) sulfate ($FeSO_4$), also known as ferrous sulfate. Iron is an essential element for the formation of a specialized *metalloprotein*, *hemoglobin*, in red blood cells. Hemoglobin is responsible for transporting oxygen from the lungs to all tissues in the body. A number of conditions can cause a low-iron condition, a deficiency known as *anemia*. Pharmaceutical companies produce a number of different over-the-counter iron supplements to help prevent this condition.

In order to determine the percentage of the Fe^{2+} ion present in a particular iron supplement, we can titrate a known concentration of potassium permanganate into an acidic solution containing the iron supplement. Upon addition of $KMnO_4$ to the acidic iron sulfate solution, the $KMnO_4$ reacts with the iron (II) sulfate. The manganese in the permanganate ion easily reduces from an initial oxidation state of +7 to +2 over the course of the reaction. The +7 form of manganese has an intense purple color, while the +2 form is colorless. The Fe^{2+} ion present in the reaction gets oxidized from +2 to +3. The solution accepting the $KMnO_4$ titrant will remain colorless until all the Fe^{2+} has reacted, at which point the solution becomes pink due to the presence of the +7 form of manganese. The balanced redox reaction in acidic solution is as follows:

$$MnO_4^- (aq) + 8H^+ (aq) + 5Fe^{2+} (aq) \rightarrow Mn^{2+} (aq) + 4H_2O(l) + 5Fe^{3+} (aq)$$

Procedure

1. Assemble your titration apparatus.
2. Place the funnel in the opening of the buret. Make sure the stopcock is in the closed position.
3. Obtain the 0.02 *M* $KMnO_4$ solution from your instructor. Carefully, and slowly, pour the $KMnO_4$ solution into the buret up to the 50-mL mark.
4. Place the 600-mL waste beaker under the buret and turn the stopcock three times to remove any air in the tip.
5. Record the volume on the buret to the nearest 0.1 mL. This will be the initial reading for trial 1.
6. Obtain an iron supplement sample from your instructor.
7. Place a weigh boat or weighing paper on the balance and zero the balance. Weigh the iron supplement and record the mass in your data table to the nearest 0.01 g or better.
8. Place the iron supplement in a 250-mL Erlenmeyer flask.
9. Measure about 50 mL of 1.0 *M* H_2SO_4 in a 100-mL graduated cylinder and pour the contents into the Erlenmeyer flask with the iron supplement. Swirl the flask until the contents of the iron supplement are completely dissolved.
10. Place the flask under the buret.
11. Slowly begin adding the $KMnO_4$ solution to the flask, one turn at a time. After each turn, swirl the flask to mix the contents.
12. Eventually, you will notice a faint yellow color appearing every time the $KMnO_4$ is added. At this point measure out about 3 mL of 2.0 *M* H_3PO_4 in your 10-mL graduated cylinder and add it to the flask. The phosphoric acid prevents the Fe^{3+} ion from turning its characteristic pale yellow color.
13. Continue with the titration, slowly adding the $KMnO_4$ solution to the flask, one turn at a time. Eventually, a faint pink color will remain after swirling. This is the endpoint of the titration. The trial is complete. Record the volume on the buret. This is the final volume for trial 1.
14. Repeat steps 7–13 two more times with another dose of the same iron supplement.
15. Test each iron supplement provided, conducting three trials each.

Experiment 17: Determination of the Percentage of Iron in Iron Supplements—
Redox Titration
Short Form Report Sheet

Your Name	

Your instructor will determine whether you will write a complete lab report for this experiment or use the following short form report sheet.

Create a data table for the three trials performed for each iron supplement. Include the iron supplement name, chemical formula of iron supplement, mass of iron supplement, initial volume of $KMnO_4$, final volume of $KMnO_4$, and total $KMnO_4$ added.

Questions

Create a table for displaying the results of the following calculations.

1. Determine the mole amounts of $KMnO_4$ used for each trial.
2. Using the balanced reaction (shown again below), determine the number of moles of Fe^{2+} present in each sample.

$$MnO_4^-(aq) + 8H^+(aq) + 5Fe^{2+}(aq) \rightarrow Mn^{2+}(aq) + 4H_2O(l) + 5Fe^{3+}(aq)$$

3. Determine the mass of Fe^{2+} present in each sample.
4. Calculate the percentage by mass of Fe^{2+} present in each iron supplement.

5. Compare the iron content of different iron supplements from data collected by the class. Rank the supplements from greatest iron content to lowest iron content.

Experiment 18
Electrochemical Series

18

Text Connections
- *General Chemistry*, Sections 12.3.1–12.3.4
- *Chemistry for Accelerated Students*, Sections 12.3.1–12.3.4

Objectives

To determine reduction potential experimentally and use experimental data to create an electrochemical series.

New Lab Skills Focus for Experiment 18

Using a voltmeter for data collection

Apparatus

filter paper, 12.5 cm	Petri dish
forceps	scissors
pencil	voltmeter

Chemicals

aluminum strips	magnesium nitrate, 1.0 M
aluminum nitrate solution, 1.0 M	nickel strips
copper strips	nickel (II) nitrate, 1.0 M
copper (II) nitrate solution, 1.0 M	silver foil
iron strips	silver nitrate, 1.0 M
iron (III) nitrate solution, 1.0 M	sodium nitrate, 1.0 M
magnesium ribbon, pieces	

Safety

Always follow the general safety practices described in the Preface for Students. In particular, the following safety precautions should be taken during this experiment:

1. Wear nitrile gloves whenever handling any substances.
2. Wear appropriate laboratory eye protection at all times.
3. Wear a laboratory apron to protect your clothing.

Background

A *voltaic cell* is a device that uses a spontaneous redox reaction to produce an electric current. A voltaic cell is physically arranged so that the oxidation and reduction half-reactions actually occur in separate compartments or half-cells. The redox electron transfer occurs by electrons flowing in an external pathway (a wire)—this is the electric current produced by the redox reaction.

The redox reaction occurs between two metals (electrodes), the *anode* and the *cathode*, in the presence of ionic solutions bearing the same metal cation. The oxidation half-reaction occurs at the anode, while the reduction half-reaction occurs at the cathode. Each half-reaction occurs in its own half-cell and the two half-cells are connected by a *salt bridge*. The salt bridge is essential for the voltaic cell to work because it completes the closed circuit for the flow of charge during the reaction. The salt bridge provides a path for charge (ions) to transfer between the electrolytes in the half-cells, thus maintaining the balance of charge between the half-cells during operation.

During the redox reaction, the anode is oxidized. As the anode loses electrons, the metal atoms become cations and enter the solution in the anode half-cell. The electrons from the anode travel through the external wire and are gained by the cations in the cathode half-cell solution. This chemistry converts these cations into metal atoms which then join the metal lattice of the cathode metal. The salt bridge, formed of a porous material, contains a soluble ionic compound, such as sodium nitrate. The Na^+ ions from the salt bridge migrate into the cathode half-cell to replace the reduced cations, while the NO_3^- ions in the salt bridge migrate into the anode half-cell to neutralize the cations released from the anode. The basic design of a voltaic cell is shown in Figure 18-1 for the oxidation of zinc (anode) and the reduction of copper (cathode).

A voltaic cell produces a voltage between the two electrodes, and this voltage is what causes the current to flow in the external conductor between the half-cells. The voltage produced by a voltaic cell depends on the materials the two electrodes are made of. Each different electrode material exhibits a certain tendency to engage in a reduction half-reaction. For a given reducing agent in a particular reduction half-reaction, we quantify this tendency with a constant called the *standard reduction potential*, symbolized as E° and measured in volts. The standard reduction potential for a material used as an electrode is usually just called the *electrode potential*, and is measured at 25°C and 1 atm, and with 1-*M* concentrations for the solutions in both half-cells.

The overall potential for a complete cell made of two half-cells is referred to as the *cell potential*. The cell potential is calculated as

$$E^\circ_{cell} = E^\circ_{cathode} - E^\circ_{anode}$$

Standard reduction potentials for many metals have been established by comparing their electric potentials to that of a reference electrode called a *standard hydrogen electrode*. The potential of the standard hydrogen electrode is assigned a voltage of zero and the electrode potentials of all other materials are established by comparison with the standard hydrogen electrode. Elec-

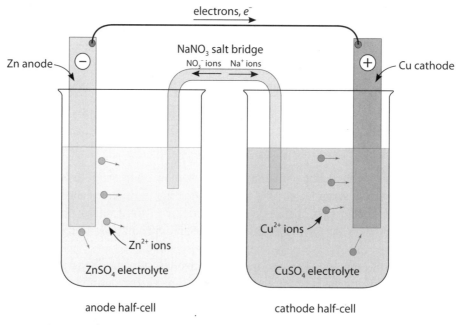

Figure 18-1. A basic Cu|Zn voltaic cell arrangement.

trode materials with more negative values of $E°$ are characteristic of anodes, while materials with more positive (less negative) values of $E°$ are used for cathodes. In order for a voltaic cell to work, the cell potential must be positive.

In this experiment you will determine the values of $E°$ for several different electrodes and then use that information to calculate the cell potential for a several different voltaic cell configurations. These data will also enable you to determine which electrode combination will produce the greatest cell potential.

Recall that the activity series of metals helps us to determine which metal will be the anode (oxidized) and which will be the cathode (reduced). The higher up a metal is on the activity series, the more readily it is willing to lose electrons (become oxidized). Metals higher in the activity series have more negative reduction potentials and are used as anodes.

Procedure

Part 1: Preparation of voltaic cells

1. Obtain a piece of filter paper. Trace the Petri dish in the filter paper and cut inside the trace, forming a paper disk that fits inside the Petri dish. Draw six small circles in a symmetrical pattern on the filter paper. Label the circles Al, Cu, Fe, Mg, Ni, and Ag outside of the circles near the border of the filter paper. Draw dotted lines connecting the circles to the center of the filter paper as shown in Figure 18-2.
2. Use scissors to cut wedges between the circles as shown in Figure 18-3.
3. Place the filter paper in the Petri dish. Add two drops of each metal-ion solution onto the corresponding circle on the filter paper; silver nitrate on silver, and so on. Add more drops if needed so the filter paper stays moist during the experiment.
4. Place a piece of each metal on the appropriate circle using forceps. Wipe the forceps with a paper towel in between each metal to avoid contaminating metals with metal ions from different metals.
5. Add several drops of sodium nitrate solution along the path of dots connecting the metals. There must be a continuous trail of sodium nitrate between each metal and the center of the circle. Add more sodium nitrate if necessary to prevent the filter paper from drying out during the experiment.

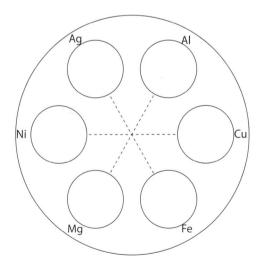

Figure 18-2. Laying out the circles and lines on the filter paper.

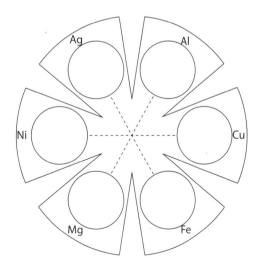

Figure 18-3. Filter paper layout with wedges cut between the circles.

Part 2: Electrode potential measurements for electrodes

1. The formation of iron metal from Fe^{3+} ions has a standard electrode potential of $E° = -0.04$ V. This value is quite close to zero, so we will use the iron in the iron/iron (III) nitrate cell as the reference electrode for measuring all the other electrode potentials. Place the leads of the voltmeter on the iron and aluminum metals, read the voltage, and record it in a data table in your lab journal. In the activity series, aluminum is a stronger reducing agent than iron and thus has a more negative electrode potential. Accordingly, placing the positive lead of the voltmeter on the iron and the negative lead on the aluminum should result in a positive voltage reading.

    Note that in making this measurement, you are essentially measuring the cell potential of a voltaic cell comprised of iron and aluminum metals in the half-cells. Iron, with $E° = -0.04$ V, is the cathode and aluminum is the anode. The voltage you read across the iron and aluminum is the cell potential. The electrode potential of the aluminum, E_{anode}, can be determined from the equation for $E°$.

2. Record which metal is the positive electrode (cathode) and which metal is the negative electrode (anode). Referring to the activity series will help with this step.[1]

3. Repeat steps 1 and 2 for the other metals (copper, magnesium, nickel, and silver) with iron as the reference electrode. Remember to prevent the filter paper from drying out by replenishing the metal ion solutions as necessary.

4. Calculate the electrode potential for each metal and record the value in your data table.

Part 3: Cell potential predictions and measurements

1. Excluding the iron reference electrode, there are 10 combinations of the remaining five metals available to test. Select two metals other than iron (such as aluminum and nickel) and use their experimental electrode potential values (calculated above in Part 2 step 4) to predict the cell potential for a voltaic cell made with these two metals in the half-cells. Record which metal should be the cathode and which should be the anode and record the predicted cell potential.

2. Measure the cell potential for the voltaic cell by touching the leads of the voltmeter to the two selected metals and record the value.

3. Repeat steps 1 and 2 for the remaining nine combinations of metals (again, excluding iron).

---

1   See Table 12-1 in *General Chemistry* or *Chemistry for Accelerated Students*. Note that although reductions involving iron ions occur twice in Table 12-1, the reduction we are using here of Fe^{3+} to Fe is not listed.

Experiment 18: Electrochemical Series
Short Form Report Sheet

Your Name	

Your instructor will determine whether you will write a complete lab report for this experiment or use the following short form report sheet.

Part 2: Electrode potential measurements for electrodes

Create a data table for the data collected in Part 2. Include the electrodes measured (iron and each of the other five metals), anode identity, cathode identity, cell potential, and calculated reduction potential for each metal.

Part 3: Cell potential predictions and measurements

Create a data table for the data collected in Part 3. Include the electrodes measured, anode identity, cathode identity, predicted cell potential, measured cell potential, and percent difference for each of the 10 cells.

Questions

1. Using the reduction potentials calculated for the metals in Part 1, list the metals in order of decreasing ability to be oxidized (that is, most negative reduction potential to most positive). Describe how well your pattern matches the activity series.

2. List the metal combinations from Part 2 in order of increasing cell potential. Describe the relationship between your list and the activity series.

Experiment 19
Synthesis of Aspirin

19

Text Connections
- *General Chemistry*, Although organic chemistry is not addressed specifically in the text, this experiment is relatively simple and would still be interesting to perform.
- *Chemistry for Accelerated Students*, Chapter 13

Objective

To synthesize an organic compound and determine the purity and percent yield of the product.

New Lab Skills Focus for Experiment 19

1. Recrystallization
2. Iron chloride purity test

Apparatus

balance
beaker, 250 mL
beaker, 600 mL (2)
Büchner funnel
Bunsen burner and hose
clamp, 3-finger, with ring stand clamp (2)
Erlenmeyer flask, 125 mL (2)
evaporating dish
filter paper (appropriate size to fit Büchner funnel)
graduated cylinder, 10 mL
graduated cylinder, 100 mL
glass stirring rod
paper towel
ring stand and 4" iron burner ring

rubber Büchner funnel stopper
spatula
test tubes, small (4)
test tube rack
test tube stopper, size #000 (2)
vacuum hose
vacuum flask, large
vacuum flask, small
wash bottle with absolute ethanol
wash bottle with distilled water (cold)
wash bottle with distilled water (≈50°C)
watch glass
weigh boat
wire gauze

Chemicals

absolute ethanol
acetic anhydride
aspirin, crushed (over-the-counter sample)
distilled water (cold)

$FeCl_3$ solution, 1%, in a dropper bottle
H_2SO_4, 18.0 M, in a dropper bottle
ice
salicylic acid

Safety

Always follow the general safety practices described in the Preface for Students. In particular, the following safety precautions should be taken during this experiment:

1. Wear nitrile gloves whenever handling any substances.
2. Wear appropriate laboratory eye protection at all times.
3. Wear a laboratory apron to protect your clothing.
4. Remember, never ingest substances used or produced in the lab.

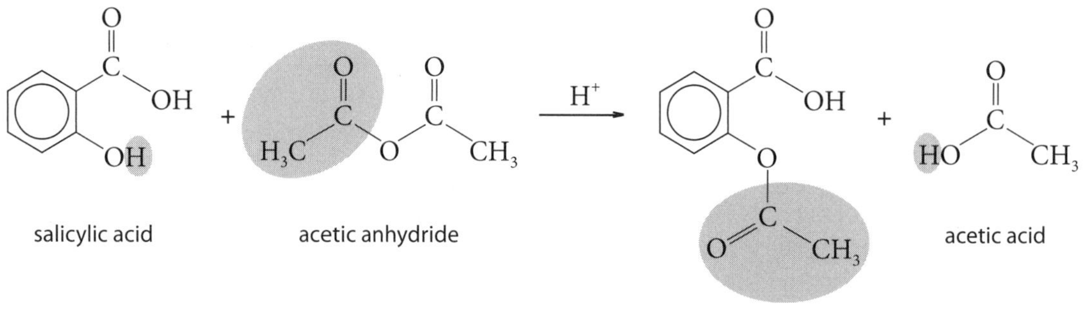

Figure 19-1. Reaction between salicylic acid and acetic anhydride.

Background

The process of *esterification* involves the synthesis of ester-containing compounds by reacting carboxylic acid compounds with alcohols in the presence of an acid. Acetylsalicylic acid, also known as aspirin, is a product of salicylic acid and acetic anhydride.

The reaction between salicylic acid and acetic anhydride, illustrated in Figure 19-1, is very straightforward. In the presence of acid, the alcohol (—OH) group in the salicylic acid reacts with the acetyl (COCH₃) group in the acetic anhydride to produce acetylsalicylic acid and acetic acid. These active groups in the molecules are shaded gray in the figure. Notice that the acetyl group on the acetic anhydride has moved to the acetylsalicylic acid, forming an ester group there.

The active ingredient of aspirin is salicylic acid. However, it possesses the undesirable properties of bitter taste and a tendency to increase the acidity in the gastrointestinal tract. Converting salicylic acid to acetylsalicylic acid helps mask the bitter flavor and acidity. Once digested, the acetylsalicylic acid converts back to salicylic acid, enters the blood stream, and functions as an effective anti-inflammatory drug, pain reliever, and fever-reducer.

In this experiment you will synthesize aspirin by reacting salicylic acid and acetic anhydride in the presence of sulfuric acid. In order to purify our aspirin sample, we will perform two rounds of crystallization. The second round of crystallization (the recrystallization) will allow for greater purity and larger aspirin crystals. As with all things in the lab, the final product of this experiment should not be ingested or used.

After synthesizing the aspirin, you will test its purity and compare the levels of purity of the first round of crystallization and the second round of crystallization (recrystallization). The compound $FeCl_3$ reacts with phenol groups (—OH groups attached to a phenyl ring) such as the —OH group on salicylic acid. $FeCl_3$ will react with phenol groups to produce a color range from green to blue and from red to violet. Thus we can use $FeCl_3$ in a test to determine the presence of unreacted salicylic acid in the aspirin sample.

Procedure

Part 1: Synthesis of aspirin

1. Prepare a hot water bath (80°C–90°C) as shown in Figure 19-2.
2. Also prepare a cold (ice) water bath as shown in Figure 19-3.
3. Label three test tubes 1, 2, 3, 4 and set them aside.
4. Place a weigh boat on the balance and zero the balance.
5. Weigh about 2 g of salicylic acid on the weigh boat and record the mass to 0.01 g or better

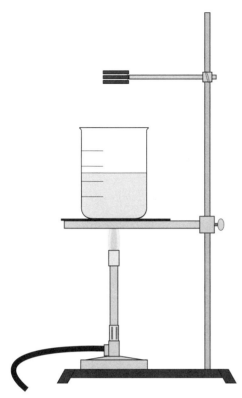

Figure 19-2. Hot water bath apparatus.

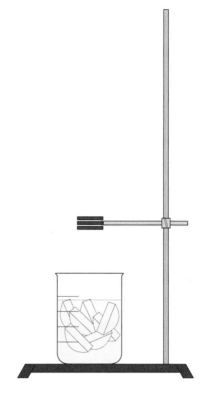

Figure 19-3. Cold water bath apparatus.

in a data table in your lab journal. Carefully add the salicylic acid to a 125-mL Erlenmeyer flask.

6. Measure about 5 mL of acetic anhydride in a 10-mL graduated cylinder. Pour the acetic anhydride into the weigh boat and carefully move the solution around with a glass stirring rod to remove any residual salicylic acid from the weigh boat.

7. Carefully pour the acetic anhydride into the 125-mL flask with the salicylic acid. Swirl the flask to mix.

8. Add five drops of 18.0 M H_2SO_4 to the flask and swirl.

9. Attach the flask securely to the clamp at the hot water bath. Lower the flask into the hot water bath and secure the clamp to the ring stand. Heat the solution for 10 minutes. The solution should turn brown-amber in color.

10. Turn off the Bunsen burner, carefully remove the flask from the hot water bath, and place it on a paper towel on the bench top.

11. Add about 10 mL of cold distilled water. Swirl the flask to mix. You should observe that the color gets lighter.

12. Attach the flask securely to the clamp in the ring stand at the cold water bath. Lower the flask into the cold water bath to allow crystallization.

13. While the solution is crystallizing, prepare the filtra-

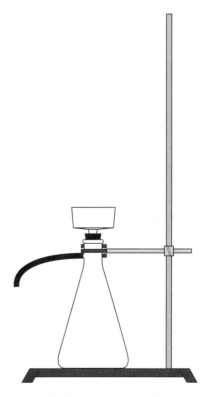

Figure 19-4. Vacuum filtration apparatus.

tion apparatus as shown in Figure 19-4.[1]

14. Once the solution has crystallized, prepare the filter paper in the Büchner funnel by adding a few milliliters of cold distilled water.
15. Pour the aspirin solution into the Büchner funnel. Rinse the flask with cold distilled water and add to the Büchner funnel again.
16. Once filtration is complete, turn off the vacuum and remove the filter paper.
17. Using a spatula, scrape the contents of the filter paper into a 250-mL beaker. Place a couple of crystals into test tube #2, stopper the test tube, and reserve them for Part 2.
18. Carefully place the filter paper into the beaker. To completely remove all crystals from the filter paper, use a wash bottle filled with absolute ethanol and wash the filter paper into the beaker containing the aspirin crystals.
19. Dissolve the aspirin in the ethanol by swirling the beaker. Add about 60 mL of warm (50°C) distilled water into the beaker. The solution may become cloudy. Stir the solution with a glass stirring rod and pour the solution into a clean 125-mL Erlenmeyer flask.
20. Attach the flask securely to the clamp in the ring stand of the cold water bath. Lower the flask into the cold water bath for recrystallization. (The flask can also be allowed to sit overnight and cool to room temperature over night. Cover the opening of flask with a watch glass.)
21. While solution is recrystallizing, place a clean Büchner funnel filter paper and watch glass on the balance and record the mass to 0.01 g or better.
22. Once recrystallization is complete, prepare the filter paper in the Büchner funnel by adding a few milliliters of cold distilled water.
23. Pour the aspirin solution into the Büchner funnel. Rinse the flask with cold distilled water and add to the Büchner funnel again.
24. Once filtration is complete, turn off the vacuum and remove the filter paper with the aspirin.
25. Place the filter paper with the aspirin on a watch glass. Allow the filter paper and aspirin to dry overnight.
26. Once the filter paper and aspirin are completely dry, record the mass of the watch glass, filter paper, and aspirin to the nearest 0.01 g or better.
27. Place a couple crystals into test tube #3, stopper the test tube, and reserve for Part 2.

Part 2: Assessing the purity of aspirin

1. Add a few crystals of salicylic acid to test tube #1.
2. Add a few crystals of the crushed pure, over-the-counter, aspirin from your instructor to test tube #4.
3. Obtain test tubes #2 and #3 from Part 1.
4. Add 1–2 drops of $FeCl_3$ solution to each test tube and record the color.

---

1   See Notes to Instructors for alternatives to using vacuum filtration.

Experiment 19: Synthesis of Aspirin
Short Form Report Sheet

Your Name	

Your instructor will determine whether you will write a complete lab report for this experiment or use the following short form report sheet.

Create a data table for the data collected in Part 1 of the experiment. Include the mass of salicylic acid, the volume of acetic anhydride, the mass of the watch glass and filter paper, and the mass of watch glass, filter paper, and aspirin.

Create a data table for Part 2 of the experiment. Include the test tube number, the contents of each tube, and the color change.

Questions

1. Determine the mass of aspirin produced in your experiment.

2. Based upon the mass of salicylic acid used and the mass of product made, calculate the theoretical yield and the percent yield of aspirin.

3. If your percent yield of aspirin is greater than 100%, explain how this could occur.

4. Why was cold water instead of hot water used to rinse the flasks during filtration?

5. Compare the two $FeCl_3$ purity tests. Was there a noticeable difference between the aspirin crystals obtained from the first round of crystallization compared to the second round of recrystallization? What does a color change signify?

6. Imagine that you find a very old bottle of aspirin at your home. Being the good chemistry student, you bring a sample from this bottle to your chemistry teacher and decide to run some tests. Using the knowledge you gained from this experiment and Experiment 1 (Identification of Substances by Physical Properties), describe the experiments you could perform to determine the purity of this old sample of aspirin. What would be your controls?

Experiment 20
Calorimetry of Organic Compounds

20

Text Connections
- *General Chemistry*, Section 8.2.7. Although organic chemistry is not addressed specifically in the text, this experiment is relatively simple and would still be interesting to perform.
- *Chemistry for Accelerated Students*, Section 6.2.7, Chapter 13. Note that this experiment is fun to perform even if Chapter 13 is not covered in the course.

Objective

To compare the caloric content of different foods.

New Lab Skills Focus for Experiment 20

Use of a simple can calorimeter

Apparatus

aluminum soda can (empty and clean)
balance
butane lighter
cork stopper, #16
glass stirring rod

graduated cylinder, 100 mL
ring stand and 3" iron burner ring
straight pin
thermometer clamp or 3-finger clamp

Chemicals

distilled water

food items (peanuts, marshmallows, crackers, dried fruit, beef jerky, cheese, etc.)

Safety

Always follow the general safety practices described in the Preface for Students. In particular, the following safety precautions should be taken during this experiment:

1. Wear nitrile gloves whenever handling any substances.
2. Wear appropriate laboratory eye protection at all times.
3. Wear a laboratory apron to protect your clothing.
4. Remember, never ingest substances used or produced in the lab.

Background

How much energy does your food have? In other words, what is the caloric content of your food? The foods we eat contain a wide variety of carbon-based compounds. As examples, carbohydrates range from the simple 6-carbon sugar known as fructose to the 1000+ -carbon glucose polymers found in starch. Triglycerides found in fats are composed of three fatty acid hydrocarbon chains, with each fatty acid chain 4 to 28 carbons long. Which types of foods provide the most energy upon consumption? When we digest food, we oxidize it, converting the energy in the food into chemical energy that our bodies can use for cellular functions. The combustion (oxidation) of glucose (a monosaccharide) occurs as follows:

$$C_6H_{12}O_6(aq) + 6O_2(g) \rightarrow 6CO_2(g) + 6H_2O(l) + \text{energy}$$

The purpose of this experiment is to utilize your calorimetry skills from your thermochemistry studies in order to determine which foods have the highest caloric (energy) content per gram. In order to accomplish this, we will once again revisit the calorimetry equation

$$Q = Cn\Delta T$$

However, in this experiment we will be applying this equation to a mass of water that is being heated. Thus, it will be more convenient to use a different form of this equation:

$$Q = c_p m \Delta T$$

In this equation, Q and ΔT represent heat and change in temperature ($T_f - T_i$) as before, m is the mass, and c_p is a parameter called the *specific heat capacity*. In the same way that the molar heat capacity, C, is defined as the amount of heat required to raise the temperature of one mole of a substance by 1°C, the specific heat capacity, c_p, is the amount of heat required to raise the temperature of one gram of a substance by 1°C. Since no chemical equations are involved in this experiment, it will be more convenient to use the specific heat capacity equation instead of the molar heat capacity equation.

The basic idea is to burn a sample of food under an aluminum can calorimeter containing a known mass of water. As the sample is burned, the heat released will be used to heat the water in the can. The energy from the food will be transferred to the water as thermal energy, causing the water temperature to rise. The specific heat capacity of water is c_p = 4.184 J/(g·°C). An energy of 4.184 joules is equivalent to 1 calorie, giving the specific heat capacity of water as c_p = 1.000 cal/ (g·°C). Using this value, the temperature rise, and the mass of water in the can, you can easily calculate how much energy the water absorbed from the combustion of a given food sample.

You should note that the labels on packages of food use dietary Calorie units (spelled with a capital "C"). One dietary Calorie is equal to 1,000 thermodynamic calories. So if your experimental results put the heat content of a marshmallow at 22,500 cal and the package lists them at 22.5 Cal each, your results are in agreement with the label on the package.

Procedure

1. As illustrated in Figure 20-1, assemble a food holder by inserting a straight pin through the center of a cork. The cork may be cut in half if it is too long. If it is too hard to push the pin through the center of the cork, try pushing the pin through the side of the cork at an angle so the top of the pin is sticking through the top of the cork.

2. Assemble the aluminum can calorimeter as shown in Figure 20-2.

3. Using a 100-mL graduated cylinder, measure 50 mL (50 g) distilled water, measure the volume of water to the nearest 0.1 mL, and enter the measurement in your lab journal.

4. Pour the water carefully into the aluminum can.

5. Use the thermometer clamp to set the ther-

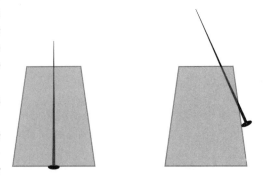

Figure 20-1. Prepare a food holder by pushing a pin through a cork through the center (left) or through the side (right).

mometer in the can. Be sure the bottom of the thermometer is not touching the bottom of the can but is submerged in the water.

6. Record the temperature of the water to the nearest 0.1°C. This is the initial temperature.

7. Carefully place a piece of food on the pin on the food holder. (Try to avoid sticking yourself with the pin. It kinda hurts.)

8. Record the mass of the food and food holder to the nearest 0.01 g.

9. Adjust the ring clamp and thermometer clamp so that the bottom of the aluminum can is 1.5 inches above the food.

10. Use the butane lighter to light the food on fire. Once the food has ignited, stop the butane lighter.

11. Once the food has burned out, wait until the thermometer reading is at its highest point, then record the temperature of the water to the nearest 0.1°C. This is the final temperature.

12. Record the mass of the food and food holder to the nearest 0.01 g.

13. Empty the water in the can and clean the bottom of the can.

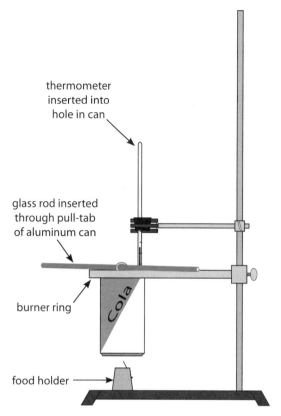

Figure 20-2. Can holder with food holder placed beneath.

14. Repeat steps 3–12 for your remaining samples. Conduct at least three trials on each type of food sample, carefully measuring the mass of each sample separately.

Experiment 20: Calorimetry of Organic Compounds
Short Form Report Sheet

Your Name	

Your instructor will determine whether you will write a complete lab report for this experiment or use the following short form report sheet.

Create a data table for the data collected in the experiment. Include the volume of water in the calorimeter, the mass of the food sample and food holder before and after burning, the mass of the food sample burned, the initial water temperature, the final water temperature, and the ΔT of the water.

Questions

1. Determine the energy content in calories/gram for each food sample.

2. Rank the foods from highest to lowest caloric content.

3. Compare your results to the nutritional label found on each food sample. Compare the amount of carbohydrate, protein, and fat in each sample.

Notes to Instructors

Experiment 1   Identification of Substances by Physical Properties

1. This experiment will most likely take two class periods or two hours to complete. In preparation for the experiment, students should be instructed to read through the procedure and prepare data tables in their lab journals. Having these tables prepared in advance will save quite a bit of time during the experiment. Moreover, when students understand the procedure well enough to prepare their data tables, they will have a much clearer view of what they are supposed to do during the experiment and will be able to begin work immediately during the laboratory time.

2. Portions of this experiment can also be performed independently to accommodate specific lessons, i.e., solubility and colligative properties lessons.

3. The instructor may choose any convenient solid and liquid substances from Table 1-1 to use for the unknown substances. Naphthalene and toluene are two substances that work well.

4. The melting point of solid substances (Part 3) procedure is designed for a laboratory that does not have a melting point apparatus available. An apparatus can be easily designed in the lab by securing a capillary tube with the solid sample to a thermometer and assembled as shown in the experiment description. Alternatively, a melting point apparatus, such as the MEL-TEMP, can be purchased and used according to the manufacturer's instructions. It is recommended to purchase capillary tubes that are closed on one end to alleviate the sealing step required if the tube is open on both ends.

5. Ideally, students should have four people in each group to enable better use of time. For example, two students can work on Part 3 while two work on Part 4. Then they can switch to perform the second trial to confirm data.

6. Lab reports should include a detailed discussion section describing their calculations, possible error, percent difference calculations, and determination of the unknown substances.

Experiment 2   Separation of Components in a Mixture

1. It is possible to complete this experiment within the class period if the apparatus is set up ahead of time and water is heated for step 3. Additionally, the evaporation step can be completed without using a Bunsen burner setup by simply allowing the sodium chloride to dry out overnight.

2. The mixture for the students is a dry mixture of sodium chloride, silicon dioxide (sand), and benzoic acid. As you prepare the mixture, be sure to write down the masses and calculate the mass percentages of the individual components in order to provide these data to students.

3. Before conducting this experiment you may wish to engage students in a classroom activity using a simpler mixture such as sodium chloride, silicon dioxide, iron filings, and poppy seeds. Students could work in groups to develop their own separation procedure, based on simple principles and common apparatus found in the laboratory. The instructor can also relate this material to a review of the scientific method.

4. If equipment for vacuum filtration is not available, gravity filtration with flute-folded filter paper may be substituted (see Experiment 6). However, the filtration will require a signifi-

cant amount of time, so the experiment will have to extend over two class periods to allow filtration to occur over night.

Experiment 3   Flame Tests and Metal Cation Identification

1. Solutions of 0.1 *M* may also be used, except for the HCl.
2. For the unknown solution instructors can either duplicate one of the known solutions, or use a solution made with a different salt that includes the same metal cation as one of the known solutions (e.g., a sulfate instead of the chloride). It is also possible to use a compound containing a completely different cation if the instructor desires the students to conduct their own research to find color charts to help with the identification. Use of a spectroscope can provide even more detailed information for each metal by separating the light into specific lines in the visible spectrum.

Experiment 4   Determining the Empirical Formula of a Copper Chloride Hydrate

If equipment for vacuum filtration is not available, gravity filtration with flute-folded filter paper may be substituted (see Experiment 6). However, the filtration will require a significant amount of time, so the experiment will have to extend over two class periods to allow filtration to occur over night.

Experiment 9   Mole Amount of a Gas

1. A "pneumatic trough" is a water tray especially designed for collecting a gas over water. Such items are usually equipped with a bracket or specially shaped bottom to allow the gas hose to enter the collection vessel. However, this specialty item is not really necessary. As shown in Figure 9-1, any deep plastic tray will work, and the collecting vessel can be supported with a ring stand and clamp.
2. Instead of using the inverted graduated cylinder for gas collection, there are manufacturers (e.g., Flinn Scientific) that make gas collecting tubes specially for the purpose. These cost significantly more than the polypropylene graduated cylinder, but gas volume measurements will be more precise. Note however that the quantity of aluminum specified for this lab will produce a larger volume of gas than any gas collection tubes can handle. Thus, use of a gas collection tube instead of a graduated cylinder will require reducing the quantity of the aluminum reactant.
3. Hydrochloric acid and acetic acid are supplied in excess for Part 1 and 2, respectively.
4. The unknown mass of sodium bicarbonate in Part 2 should be near 1.0 g.

Experiment 10   Metathesis Reactions

The four unknown solutions are simply unidentified solutions from the eight previously tested in Part 1 and 2. Place these four solutions in dropper bottles labeled, "Unknown Solution #1," etc.

Experiment 11   Acid-Base Titration

Preparation of the unknown molarity solution of NaOH (300 mL for each lab group):

The NaOH solution will be 0.1 *M*. Prepare as follows:

1. First prepare a 12 M stock solution of NaOH by adding 500 mL distilled water at room

temperature to 240 g of low-carbonate NaOH in a 2-L beaker.

2. Boil enough water to provide 100 mL to each student lab station. Once the water is cooled, aliquot 120 mL into a flask with a rubber stopper. Add 1 mL of 12 M stock solution and shake vigorously for 1 minute, with the stopper firmly in place.

3. The water is boiled to remove carbon dioxide. Additionally, the flask must be stopped when not in use to prevent carbon dioxide from the air reacting with NaOH and thus changing the molarity. NaOH readily reacts with CO_2 to produce sodium bicarbonate.

Note: You can use this standardized solution of NaOH for the following experiment (Experiment 12, Effectiveness of Antacids) if you prepare enough to supply each station with an additional 75–100 mL.

Preparation of CO₂-free water for KHP solutions:

1. Each student station will need 400 mL of boiled and cooled distilled water in order to make the KHP solution in Part 1 and the unknown solution in Part 2.

2. Once the water has been boiled to remove any CO_2, cover the opening of the flask or beaker.

Preparation of burets for use:

   This can also be done by the students, but if time is limited, this can be performed by the instructor prior to the experiment.

1. Clean a 50-mL buret with soap solution and buret brush and thoroughly rinse with tap water.

2. Rinse the buret with 10 mL distilled water at least five times.

3. Test the stopcock to ensure it does not leak and turns freely.

Preparation of KHP unknown:

The unknown solid solution should be approximately 60% KHP solid to 40% NaCl solid by weight. The students will need about 10 g total per station.

Experiment 12   Effectiveness of Antacids

Preparation of antacids:

1. You may choose to have each lab station test every antacid you provide, or have each station test one and compare the data across the class. Regardless, preparation of the samples is similar. Ideally, it's easiest to use antacids that come as chewable, white tablets. Tablets with color can be used, it will just require a good eye to catch the color change upon neutralization. Each lab station should get three doses so they can test each antacid in three trials. A mortar and pestle can be used to break up the tablet so it dissolves more easily in the acid. Note that Milk of Magnesia is extremely effective. This may be a good antacid to use as a demonstration after the experiment because it is able to neutralize a high volume of acid, more than what is required in this experiment.

2. Prepare a table of information for each antacid tested in the experiment, including the active antacid ingredient and the dose in milligrams so students can calculate the concentration of each antacid.

3. Some antacids contain more than one active ingredient. For example, Gaviscon contains aluminum hydroxide and magnesium hydroxide. Others may contain a base and a buffer. As long as all the information is provided to the students, they should be able to calculate the overall antacid concentration in solution.

4. The experiment will be more interesting to the students if you communicate to them beforehand that the ultimate goal is to determine the most effective antacid. Students love competition, even if it is between antacids!

Preparation of buret for use:

This preparation can be done by the students, but if time is limited, this can be performed by the instructor prior to the experiment.

1. Clean a 50-mL buret with soap solution and buret brush and thoroughly rinse with tap water.
2. Rinse the buret with 10 mL distilled water at least five times.
3. Test the stopcock to ensure it does not leak and turns freely.

Experiment 13   Calorimetry and Hess's Law

1. The sketch in Figure 13-1 was drawn based on two small polystyrene cups. Using a medium-sized cup nestled inside a small cup provides an air layer between the cups which provides additional insulation.
2. For the calorimeter lid, you can use a regular coffee cup lid. For better insulation, you can make a "stopper" lid by cutting a thick piece of Styrofoam so it fits into the top of the upper cup like a cork, as suggested in Figure 13-1.
3. For the stirrer, a length of copper wire may be used. For better thermal insulation, use the plastic wand from a bottle of children's bubble blowing solution. As shown in Figure NT-1, you can cut off the loops and glue one of them back onto the rod at a right angle using an adhesive such as water-proof Super Glue.

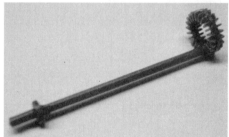

Figure NT-1. Bubble wand from bubble blowing solution (top). Modified bubble wand (bottom).

Experiment 14   Rate Law Determination for the Acid-Catalyzed Iodination of Acetone

The starch solution is 1% starch by mass. Any pure starch, such as the 100% pure cornstarch available at grocery stores, may be used. Prepare the solution by mixing 1.0 g starch in 99.0 g distilled water.

Experiment 15   Le Châtelier's Principle

The boiling water bath and ice water bath can be placed in a centralized location or you can have one available for each lab station.

Experiment 16   Titration Curves and K_a

This experiment will be easier to perform if a magnetic stir plate is used to stir the solutions during titration. If magnetic stirrers are not available, students can manually swirl the beakers.

Calibration of pH meter:

Portable pH meters must be calibrated before each use, typically with a substance such as tomato juice. Be sure to calibrate all pH meters according to manufacturer instructions immediately prior to the experiment. Standardized pH buffer solutions for calibration are available from Flinn Scientific and other science suppliers.

Preparation of buret for use:

This can also be done by the students, but if time is limited, this can be performed by the instructor prior to the experiment.
1. Clean a 50-mL buret with soap solution and buret brush and thoroughly rinse with tap water.
2. Rinse the buret with 10 mL distilled water at least five times.
3. Test the stopcock to ensure it does not leak and turns freely.

Analysis of titration curves:

The webpage listed below is an additional resource showing how to analyze and interpret their titration data.

   http://people.bridgewater.edu/~koverway/courses/CHEM162/ppts/TitrationCurves.6.pdf

Experiment 17   Determination of the Percentage of Iron in Iron Supplements—Redox Titration

1. Ideally, each student lab group will test three or four different iron supplements. However, to save time, you might consider having each of the student lab groups test one iron supplement, with each group testing a different one. Data can the be shared among groups for the ranking activity in the questions.
2. Many iron supplements simply state the active ingredient as "iron". Although the majority of iron supplements are iron (II) sulfate (or ferrous sulfate), it is best to double check the chemical formula.
3. As with Experiment 12, the experiment will be more interesting to the students if you communicate to them beforehand that the ultimate goal is to determine the supplement containing the most iron. Students love competition, even if it is between iron supplements!

Experiment 19   Synthesis of Aspirin

1. If equipment for vacuum filtration is not available, gravity filtration with flute-folded filter paper may be substituted (see Experiment 6). However, the filtration will require a significant amount of time, so the experiment will have to extend over two class periods to allow filtration to occur over night. Cover the funnel with a watch glass.
2. The $FeCl_3$ solution is easily prepared by adding 0.1 g $FeCl_3$ to 9.9 mL of distilled water.